中华美食系列 1

简易家常菜
Everyday Dishes

林淑莲 著

外文出版社
Foreign Languages Press

编者的话

俗话说："民以食为天"。吃饭是人们每天必不可少的大事。随着人们生活水平的提高，吃饭已不再是解决饥饿问题，而成了生活中的一项享受。饮食文化作为中国文化的一个重要组成部分，在世界文化舞台上占有越来越重要的地位。

在本书中，我们精选了118道家常菜，配以560余幅精美的彩色图片，采用图示的方法分步骤讲解，使您减少摸索的时间，尽快享受到烹调美食的乐趣。

闲暇之余，去超市买些鱼肉、青菜，回到家中按图索"骥"，相信您一定会以愉快的心情，遨游于厨艺天地之间，让美味佳肴之香温暖全家人的心房与胃肠。

本书文字汉英对照，喜爱中国菜的外国朋友，拥有此书，潜心习练，定会成为中国菜的烹调大师。

Editor's Note

As the saying goes, "People regard food as their prime want." People cannot survive without food. Along with the improvement of people's life, eating becomes a form of entertainment. As a part of the national culture, Chinese cuisine has become more important in world culture as a whole.

In this book, we have chosen 118 home-style dishes, with over 560 colored pictures. It explains how to make the dishes step by step, with the help of sketches. In this way, you can become proficient in Chinese cuisine in the shortest time possible.

Buy fish and vegetables when you have time, and cook the dishes with the help of the sketches. You will be happy in the kitchen, and your family will appreciate your efforts.

This book is published in bilingual format. Foreign friends who are interested in Chinese cuisine may be confident that they too can become skilled chefs in the tradition of Chinese cuisine.

烹调中所用的火候简介

1. 炸、溜、爆、炒等均用旺火，菜肴特点为嫩、脆、酥。
2. 烧、焖、煨、扣、炖等均先用大火,后用小火烹制, 这种方法必须先用大火把材料烧至半熟，使材料上色后再用小火煮熟。
3. 汆、涮、熬、蒸等烹调方法所采用的火力，应根据材料而定，一般质嫩易碎者宜用小火，质老而又体大者则用大火。
4. 煎、贴均以少量油作为传热方法，其菜肴特点为外香酥、里软嫩，具有浓厚的油香味，宜用温火。
5. 注意掌握油温，材料过油是菜肴在烹调前一项重要的准备工作，也是制作过程中常用的方法，一道菜品质的好、坏与过油关系非常大，加热时间掌握不好，那么菜肴品质就达不到标准。

芡汁的种类和用途

　　芡汁是指烹调过程中所加入的液体调味品和淀粉的总称。

　　芡汁按其稠度分为浓芡、薄芡两类，若按调制方法又可分为碗芡（对调味汁芡）、跑马芡（任芡）两种。

　　1. 碗芡

　　即各种调味料和水淀粉同放一个碗内溶合，适于用旺火爆、炒、溜各种菜肴。

　　2. 跑马芡

　　即水淀粉,适用于烧、烩、扒、扣等烹调方法,菜肴起锅前加入。

刀工的基本常规

一、基本要求:

1. 厨师所用菜墩要干净整洁，刀口要锋利，必备一条洁净的抹布，工作时要求干净利落。
2. 精神要集中、专心一致，操刀时要运用自如，落刀时要稳、准、狠、匀。
3. 必须根据材料的特点来决定相应的加工方法，然后用刀将材料切成整齐划一、清爽利落并符合烹调要求的形状。
4. 要根据材料的性质采用不同刀法（例如牛、羊肉要横切，鸡肉要顺切）。
5. 合理使用材料，以便物尽其用，减少损耗。

二、用刀的规矩:

1. 厨师要牢记刀和墩是不分离的，也就是说，厨师不能持刀到别处去，用后必须摆放在固定的容器内。
2. 刀若暂时不用，要将刀刃朝外前方放在墩子中央，刀把刀刃不能超出墩子边沿，以免伤到人。
3. 杜绝持刀玩耍，以防误伤。
4. 爱护刀墩，刀用后宜刷洗擦干，以防生锈，若长期不用，一定要擦油保存。

烹调中用火的经验

　　火候是烹调菜肴的关键，对于菜肴质量起着决定性作用，也是衡量厨师技术水平的重要标准。

　　烹调不同的菜肴需运用不同的火候，这是每位厨师必须掌握的，但有一个普遍的规律，即材料加热时间短则嫩，时间长则透、时间久则烂。如何做到嫩而不生、透而不老、烂而不化，那就要看厨师的水平了。

　　厨师掌握火候的关键在于观察火力，充分了解材料性质和受热的变化，以及所加工材料的质地，刀口粗细等等。

Introduction for Degree of Heating

1. Fry, saute and add thick sauce, fry briefly, stir fry: Cook by high heat to make the dish tender and crisp.
2. Roast, stew, simmer: Cook by high heat first till half done, then colour the dishes, turn to simmer later on till well done.
3. Evaporate, boil, steam: It depends on the ingredients. If it's tender and fragile, cook by simmer, if it's hard and big, cook by high heat then.
4. Decoct: Cook by temperate with less oil to make the inside of the dish tender, and the surface will be crisp.
5. Be care of the degree of heating: It's the most important step before cooking. Also it can decide whether the dish is going to be successful or fail.

How to Make and How to Use the Thick Sauce

It's made by cassava starch with water. Usually combine it with dish to thicken the taste of the dish. We can divide the thick sauce into two different kinds by the way how it was made.

1. Bowl thick sauce: Mix all the condiments with cassava starch and water in a bowl, pour them into the dish, fry by high heat.
2. Temporary thick sauce: Mix all the condiments with cassava starch and water first, dressing it on the top of the dish when it is ready to serve.

The Basic Rules of Using Knife

A. Basic Requirements:
1. The chopping board has to be very clean, the knife has to be sharp, it is necessary to prepare a nice clean towel too.
2. Be absolutely concentrate on your work. When you use the knife, stable, on mark, nice shape are things you need to be careful.
3. Cook each single ingredient by its own character, cut it into the right shape which fits the dish's style.
4. Cut the ingredient by its natural line.
5. Use everything useable, do not waste.

B. Basic Rules:
1. Remember, knife and chopping board can not be apart. Don't take the knife to go anywhere far from the chopping board —— where it should be. After using the knife, put it in a exact safty place.
2. When the knife is not in use, leave it in the centre of the chopping board to avoid accidents.
3. Never play the knife to avoid any accidentally injure.
4. Cherish and do good protecting to your chopping board. If you are not using it for a long term, make sure that it's very clean and has been settled in a nice place.

Experience of Heating

It is the most important key for cooking. It can decide whether the dish is going to be successful or fail, it also can tell how the cook has done.

Cook different dish by different heat. Cook for just a short time, the dish will be tender. cook for a long time, the dish will be well-done. How to cook a famous dish tender but not rare, not tough, and not over-done, it depends on the cook's skill. A good cook will see the heat, knowing what will happen when a single ingredient meets the heat, knowing each ingredient's character and the way of cutting.

目 录　CONTENTS

葱油鸡

【材料】
鸡……半只（或鸡腿2只）
香菜……………… 适量
(A)料：葱、姜丝各半杯。
(B)料：酒、盐各适量。
(C)料：葱、姜、酒1大匙。

【作法】
❶ 鸡先氽烫去血水，再将半锅水烧开，放入(C)料及鸡，中火煮约15分钟，熄火焖10分钟，待汤稍凉取出，并在鸡身抹少许(B)料。
❷ 鸡切块摆入盘中，将(A)料铺于其上。
❸ 热3汤匙油淋在鸡块上，即可盛出享用。

Scallion Chicken

【Ingredients】
Half a chicken (or 2 drumstick), parsley
(A)½ cup of sliced scallion and ginger
(B)wine, salt
(C)1 tbsp. scallion, ginger and wine

【Methods】
❶Blanch the chicken, boil ½ pot of water then put (C) and chicken in for 15 min. turn off heat for 10 min. remove them when the soup cold, then spread a dash of seasoning (B) on.
❷Spread (A) on chicken.
❸Pour 3 tbsp of boiling oil on the chicken and serve.

蚝油凤翼

【材料】

鸡翅膀…………………12 只
清水………………………1 杯
香油………………………少 许
油菜………………………数 棵
(A)料：葱 2 根、姜 3 片、蒜
　　　 头 2 颗。
(B)料：酱油、糖、酒、蚝油
　　　 适量。

【作法】

❶ 鸡翅膀加入(A)、(B)料略腌。

❷ 用 2 大匙油将已腌泡过的
　鸡翅炒至变色且无血水流
　出（吃起来才不会有腥
　味）。

❸ 腌泡过的(A)、(B)料加入 1
　杯清水，倒入和鸡翅同
　烧，烧至汗浓稠，熄火。

❹ 用滚水氽烫油菜（油菜如
　太大可对半切）捞出，排
　列于盘边，鸡翅再分别置
　于盘中，最后淋上锅中之
　酱汁及数滴香油，即可上
　桌。

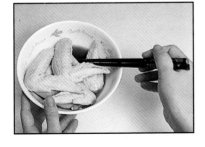

Oyster Sauce and Chicken Wings

【Ingredients】

12 chicken wings
1 cup of water, sesame oil, rapes
(A)2 scallion, 3 pieces of ginger, 2 garlic
(B)soy sauce, sugar, wine, oyster sauce

【Methods】

❶Mix chicken wings with (A) and (B) for minutes.

❷Fry the wings in 2 tbsp. oil till white and no blood.

❸Add (A)、(B) and a cup of water, then cook till gravy thicken.

❹Blanch the vegetable and arrange it on a plate, put the wings on, after that, pour the remaining sauce and a dash of sesame oil over them.

13

咖哩鸡

Curry Chicken

【材料】
鸡腿 …………………… 2 只
洋葱 …………………… 1 个
胡萝卜 ………………… 1 根
马铃薯 ………………… 2 个
咖哩块 ………………… 150 克

【作法】
❶ 鸡腿切成块，先在滚水中烫除血水。
❷ 用2大匙油拌炒鸡块，肉变色时再加入洋葱（切条状）胡萝卜及马铃薯（切小块）同炒，并加入5~6碗水煮约25分钟，鸡块稍烂时，加入剥成小块的咖哩小火续煮至浓稠。

【Ingredients】
2 drumstick, 1 onion, 1 carrot, 2 potatoes, 150g. curry

【Methods】
❶First, chop and blanch the drumstick.
❷Fry chicken、chopped onion、carront in 2 tbsp. oil, then add 5~6 bowls water to cook for 25 min. After that, add curry and cook in low heat till thicken.

箭笋肉丝

Fried Bamboo Shoot with Sliced Meat

【材料】
箭笋 ……………………250 克
肉丝 ……………………200 克
辣椒 ………………………1 个
蒜末 ………………………1 大匙
葱 …………………………2 根切段
(A)料：淀粉、酱油。
(B)料：糖、豆瓣辣酱、酱油各适量。

【作法】
❶ 肉丝拌入(A)料腌10分钟，用3匙油炒散蒜末及肉丝，盛起备用。
❷ 余油留锅内，先炒箭笋，再倒入肉丝及(B)料及少许清水，拌炒均匀即可盛出。

【Ingredients】
250g. bamboo shoot, 200g. sliced meat, 1 red chili, 1 tbsp. chopped garlic. 2 scallion
(A)cornstarch, soy sauce
(B)sugar, hot soy bean paste, soy sauce

【Methods】
❶ Slice the meat and mix with (A) for 10 min.
❷ Fry sliced meat and chopped scallion in 3 tbsp. oil. Remove. Fry bamboo shoots in remaining oil, add sliced ment、(B) and some Water, fry well and serve.

红烧狮子头

【材料】

猪肉馅·················500 克

(A)料：葱、姜末、淀粉、胡椒粉、酱油适量。

(B)料：大白菜（或生菜）约500 克，切成大块。

(C)料：酱油、清水、酒适量。胡萝卜丝、香菜少许。

【作法】

❶ 猪肉馅和(A)料充分拌匀，并摔打至有弹性（炸时才不致松散），做成大小相同的肉丸。

❷ 烧热半锅油，将肉丸倒入，油炸至金黄。

❸ 炒锅留些许油略炒大白菜及胡萝卜丝，再将炸好的肉丸倒入，并加入(C)料同烧，中火焖煮10分钟，淋上水淀粉勾芡即可。

Pork Ball Stew

【Ingredients】

500g. minced pork

(A)scallion, chopped ginger, cornstarch, pepper, soy sauce

(B)500g. Cabbage, trim it into pieces

(C)soy sauce, water, wine, carrot strips, parsley

【Methods】

❶Mix minced pork with (A), make into balls.

❷ Heat half pot of oil, put pork balls in and fry till golden.

❸Fry cabbage and carrot strip in a little oil, then put pork balls in and add (C) to cook for 10 min. Thicken with cornstarch mixture.

苦瓜镶肉汤

【材料】
苦瓜……………………1 根
肉馅…………………500 克
(A)料：酒、盐、胡椒粉各少
　　许，水淀粉 1 大匙。
(B)料：高汤 6 杯，盐、味精
　　少许。

【作法】
❶ 苦瓜洗净，切宽圈状，在
　苦瓜内侧抹少许干淀粉。
❷ 肉馅拌入(A) 料后，适量塞
　入每个苦瓜圈内并抹平。
❸ 将已塞肉的苦瓜置锅内，
　注入(B) 料，以中火炖煮
　约 25 分钟即可。

Stuffed Bitter Gourd Soup

【Ingredients】
1 bitter gourd, 500g. minced
meat
(A)wine, salt, pepper, 1 tbsp.
　cornstarch mixture
(B)6 cups of stock, salt, mono-
　sodium glutamate

【Methods】
❶Chean the bitter gourd, cut
　it into circularity. Dredge
　each bitter gourd with a
　little dry cornstarch inside.
❷Mix minced meat with
　(A) (stuff a little minced
　meat mixture in each bit-
　ter gourd)
❸Put the stuffed bitter gourd
　in a pot and add (B), then
　stew in medium heat for 25
　min.

肉末拌饭

【材料】
肉馅‥‥‥‥‥‥‥‥‥500 克
(A)料：葱花、油葱各1大匙、
　　酱黄瓜切碎 ¼ 杯
(B)酒1大匙、酱油3大匙、糖
　　少许。

【作法】
❶ 用3大匙油炒散肉馅，再
　加入(A)料炒匀。
❷ 加入(B)料及少量水烧数
　分钟即可盛出，拌饭时加
　些香菜更觉美味。

Minced Meat Rice

【Ingredients】
500g. minced meat
(A)1 tbsp. chopped scallion,
　1tbsp. fried chopped onion,
　¼ cup chopped cucumber
(B)1 tbsp. rice wine, 3 tbsp.
　soy sauce, sugar

【Methods】
❶Fry minced meat in 3 tbsp.
　oil, add (A)
❷Add (B) and a little water
　and cook for minutes. Pour-
　parsley on rice and serve.

猪血大肠汤

【材料】
猪血‥‥‥‥‥‥‥‥‥1 大块
煮烂的大肠‥‥‥‥‥半杯
(A)料：味精、盐适量。
(B)料：酸菜丝、嫩姜丝、韭
　　菜切段。
(C)料：胡椒粉、炸过的洋葱
　　末各适量。

【作法】
❶ 猪血切块，汆烫去腥，捞
　起，和已煮烂的大肠盛起
　备用。
❷ 备一锅高汤，水滚倒入猪
　血和大肠，并加入(A)料，
　续放(B)料，盛出食用时再
　撒下(C)料。

Pig Blood & Large Intestine Soup

【Ingredients】
1 piece of pig of blood, ½ cup
well - done large intestine
(A)a pinch of monosodium
　glutamate and salt
(B)sliced Pickled cabbage,
　ginger, chopped leek
(C)pepper, fried chopped on-
　ion

【Methods】
❶Chop and blanch the pig
　blood and remove.
❷Put pig blood and large in-
　testine in stock when it is
　boiling. Add (A) and (B).
　Sprinkle (C) over it before
　serve.

21

菠萝炒饭

【材料】
菠 萝 ……………………… 半 个
冷饭 ………………………2 碗
蛋 …………………………1 个
(A) 料：火腿切丁、煮熟毛豆
　　　各适量。
(B) 料：盐、酱油、味精少许。
(C) 料：肉松、葱花适量。

【作法】
❶ 菠萝对切（只用半个，装
　饭用）将果肉挖出切丁备
　用。
❷ 起油锅，将蛋炒散，放入
　(A)料和切好的菠萝、火腿
　丁及干饭拌炒。
❸ 炒饭拌炒均匀后，加入(B)
　料续炒。
❹ 炒饭置于挖空的菠萝里并
　撒下(C)料即成。

Pineapple Rice

【Ingredients】
½ Pineapple, 2 bowls of cold
rice, 1 egg
(A)ham cubes, well-done bean
(B)salt, soy sauce, monoso-
　　dium glutamate
(C)fried pork flakes, chopped
　　scallion

【Methods】
❶cut the pineapple vertically
　into halves (just use half of
　it for stuffing rice). Remove
　the pulp and cut it into
　cubes.
❷Scramble the egg, add (A),
　pineapple cubes, diced ham
　and rice, stir well.
❸After blending, add (B) and
　stir.
❹Scoop fried rice in the pine-
　apple case, then sprinkle(C).

酥炸鸡腿

【材料】

小鸡腿……………10 只

(A) 料：酒、酱油、胡椒粉、
糖各适量。蛋黄 2 个、地
瓜粉 1 盘。

【做法】

❶ 洗净小鸡腿以(A)料腌 20
分种。

❷ 热足量的油，以备炸鸡腿
用。

❸ 腌好之鸡腿，以蛋黄拌匀，
沾地瓜粉后油炸至金黄即
可。

※油锅温度不宜过高，免得
外焦内生。

Fried Little Drumsticks

【Ingredients】

10 little drumsticks

(A)wine, soy sauce, pepper,
sugar, 2 yolk, 1 dish tapioca

【Methods】

❶Clean the durmsticks and
marinate with (A) for 20
min.

❷Warm ½ pot of oil for fry-
ing the drumsticks.

❸Mix the durmsticks with
yolk and dredge tapioca,
then fry them till golden.

西芹鲜鱼片

Fried Celery with Fillet

【材料】
白色鱼肉……………250 克
西洋芹菜…………4 大根
　　　　　　（去纤维、切段）
姜片……………少许
胡萝卜丝……………适量
(A)淀粉、酒、酱油、糖。
(B) 盐、味精少许。

【作法】
❶ 鱼肉切条状，拌入(A)料，腌片刻。
❷ 姜片用3大匙油爆香后取出，续将鱼片下锅炒熟，盛出备用。
❸ 用2大匙油快炒切段的西洋芹，倒入鱼条，即加入(B)料，炒匀盛出。

【Ingredients】
250g. fillet, 4 celery, sliced ginger, sliced carrot
(A)cornstarch, wine, soy sauce, sugar
(B)a pinch of salt, monosodium glutamate

【Methods】
❶Slice the fillet, mix with (A) for minutes.
❷Fry sliced ginger in 3 tbsp. oil until fragrant, add the fillet, Remove.
❸Fry chopped celery in 2 tbsp oil, stir and put the fillet together, then add (B).

- -

油豆腐镶肉

Struffed Bean Curd

【材料】
油豆腐………………10 个
肉馅………………300 克
(A)料：葱、姜末各½大匙、淀粉适量。
(B) 胡萝卜、香菜少许。
(C)酱油、水、酒、糖各适量。

【作法】
❶ 肉馅和(A)料混合拌匀。
❷ 将油豆腐剥开一小洞塞入已拌好之肉馅。
❸ 盖过油豆腐的水量加入(C)料，和油豆腐烧约10多分钟，汤汁稍干，将油豆腐取出，余汁用水淀粉勾芡，淋于油豆腐上，并以(B)料点缀即成。

【Ingredients】
10 pieces of bean curd, 300g. minced meat
(A)cornstarch, ½ tbsp. minced scallion and ginger
(B)carrot, parsley
(C)soy sauce, water, wine, sugar

【Methods】
❶Mix minced meat with (A).
❷Dig a hole from the bean curd and stuff a little minced meat in.
❸Fry bean curd and pour more water, then add (C) to cook for 10 min. till thicken. Remove the bean curd to a plate. Thicken remaining sauce with cornstarch, and pour it on the bean curd, then sprinkle a dash of (B) before serving.

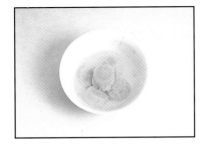

干贝芥菜

【材料】

芥菜…………1棵（切片状）
大蒜…………2颗（拍碎）
干贝…………3~5个
　　　　（依大小酌量增减）
味精、水淀粉………少许

【作法】

❶ 芥菜稍烫熟，捞出冲冷水，沥干备用。

❷ 干贝用半碗水浸泡1小时，再放入蒸锅蒸软，放凉撕丝备用。

❸ 用3匙油将大蒜爆香捞出，放入烫熟之芥菜拌炒，撒上干贝丝及倒入蒸干贝的汁（因稍有碱味，可酌量增减），调味，并以水淀粉勾芡即可。

Fried Mustard with Scallop

【Ingredients】

1 mustard (slice into pieces), 2 garlic, 3~5 scallop, monosodium glutamate, cornstarch mixture

【Methods】

❶ Blanch mustard, rinse under cold water and drain.

❷ Soak scallop in ½ bowl of water for 1 hour and steam till soft. Tear the scallop into strips.

❸ Fry chopped garlic in 2 tbsp. oil till fragrant, add mustard, sprinkle the scallop strips and pour the juice of it in. Thicken with cornstarch mixture.

串烤

【材料】

鸡肉、青椒、 洋葱、油豆腐、天妇萝※、口蘑（以上材料要切块状）。

综合调味：酱油5大匙、蒜泥½大匙，糖、香油1小匙、白芝麻适量。

※天妇萝是日本一种家常菜。罗卜、茄子、辣椒、鱼、虾等裹上面包渣，放在油里炸。

【作法】

❶将所有材料切块依序串入竹签。

❷用毛刷在每串材料上刷匀综合调味酱，用烤箱或烤肉架烤均可（火不要太大，免得内生外焦）中途可再沾一次酱汁续烤。

• •

B.B.Q.

【Ingredients】

Chicken, green bell pepper, onion, bean curd, tempura, mushroom

Mixture sauce: 5 tbsp. soy sauce, ½ tbsp. mashed garlic, sugar, 1 tbsp sesame oil, white sesame seeds

【Methods】

❶Put the ingredients on the skewers.

❷Brush mixture sauce over the kebobs, then put them on the barbecue or oven.

干煎鲑鱼

Pan Fried Salmon

【材料】
鲑鱼……1大片（或2小片）
柠檬………………2 片
盐……………… 少许

【作法】
❶ 鲑鱼洗净，用餐巾纸吸干水分，抹少许盐腌20分钟，再将盐分轻轻冲除（以免太咸）。
❷ 锅中倒入少许油（鲑鱼本身油质较多，因此不需用太多油煎），以中火将鱼片两面煎熟，盛于盘中，撒些椒盐，再挤些柠檬汁即可。

【Ingredients】
Salmon fillet, 2 slices of lemon, salt

【Methods】
❶ Clean the fillet, spread a dash of salt on it for 20 min. then rinse it to remove salt.
❷ Fry fillet in a little oil till both side is golden. Remove it to a plate. Sprinkle a pinch of pepper and squeeze lemon juice over it.

鲜美蒸蛋

Steamed Egg

【材料】
蛋………………5 个
(A)料：高汤2½杯、盐1小匙。
(B) 料：平菇、蛤蜊、虾仁。
(C) 香菜适量。

【作法】
❶ 蛋打散，加入(A)料拌匀（不可用热高汤），放入电锅蒸，锅内置2½杯的水，锅盖要留一缝隙。
❷ 水快干时，再将(B)料置于蒸蛋上，待开关跳起，取出，撒些香菜即可上桌。

【Ingredients】
5 eggs.
(A)2½ cup stock, 1 tbsp. salt
(B)mushroom, clam, shrimp
(C)Parsley

【Methods】
❶ Beat the eggs in a bowl and mix with (A) (don't use hot stock), then put the bowl in the steamer' pour 2½cup of water in the steamer. Let the cap of steamer ajar.
❷ When the water almost dry off, put (B) on the steamed egg, then steam completely. Sprinkle a dash of parsley before serving.

清蒸蟹

【材料】
蟹⋯⋯⋯⋯⋯⋯⋯⋯3 只
(A) 料：葱 3 根、姜数片。
(B) 料：醋 2 大匙、姜末 1 大匙。

【作法】
❶ 将蟹壳剥开，去除内脏并洗净，上置(A)料，放入蒸锅蒸熟。
❷ 蒸好的蟹切块置盘中，食用时再沾(B)料即可。

Steamed Crab

【Ingredients】
3 Crabs
(A)3 scallion, sliced ginger
(B)2 tbsp. vinegar, 2 tbsp. minced ginger

【Method】
❶Clean the crabs, add (A) and steam them.
❷Cut the steamed crabs and serve with (B).

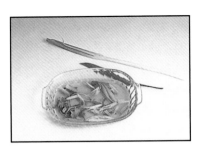

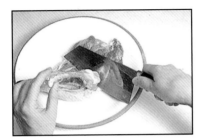

铁板烧

【材料】

牛肉片、鸡腿肉去骨、青椒、洋葱、鲜香菇、玉米块、天妇萝、绿豆芽、草虾等（材料可依个人喜爱自由选择）。

(A) 料：酱油、酒、糖、蒜末、白芝麻各适量。

(B) 蛋黄1个、酱油、糖、醋各适量。

【作法】

❶ 肉类用(A)料腌泡20分钟，备用。

❷ 豆芽菜用奶油及椒盐混合，以锡箔纸包裹，备用。

❸ 在铁板上倒入色拉油，将所有材料放在铁板上煎烤，包锡箔纸的豆芽菜直接置于铁板上烤。

❹ 调和(B)料，做为沾食之用。

Teppanyaki

【Ingredients】

Sliced beef, drumstick (remove the bone), green bell pepper, onion, mushroom, corn cubes, tempura, bean sprouts, shrimp (anything you like)

(A) soy sauce, wine, sugar, minced garlic, white sesame seeds

(B) 1 yolk, soy sauce, sugar, vinegar

【Method】

❶ Marinate the meat with (A) for 20 min.

❷ Mix bean sprouts with butter and salt, then wrap them in tinfoil.

❸ Pour some oil over the iron plate, fry all of the ingredients on it, bake the tinfoil stuff on the iron plate.

❹ Mix (B) well for dipping.

香蒜鸡胗

Garlic Chicken Gizzard

【材料】

鸡胗⋯⋯⋯⋯⋯⋯10 个

(A)料：酱油 5 大匙、酒 1 大匙、清水 3 杯、糖少许、卤味包一包。

(B)料：香油、蒜末、盐少许。

【作法】

❶ 用滚水氽烫鸡胗，去血水备用。

❷ 烧开(A)料，放入鸡胗，以中火煮约 25 分钟，熄火置锅内，待凉后切片拌(B)料即可。

【Ingredients】

10 gizzard

(A)5 tbsp. soy sauce, 1 tbsp. wine, 3 cups of water, sugar, 1 spice bag

(B)sesame oil, chopped garlic, salt

【Methods】

❶Blanch the gizzard.

❷Boil (A) and add gizzard, then cook under medium heat for 25 min. Slice the gizzard after it getting cold, dress with (B).

凉拌西芹

Celery Salad

【材料】

西洋芹菜⋯⋯⋯⋯⋯⋯半棵

(A)料：胡萝卜丝、嫩姜丝适量。

(B)料：盐、味精、香油各少许。

【作法】

❶ 西洋芹去除纤维切段，在滚水中氽烫，捞出冲冷水，沥干水分备用。

❷(A)料用少量盐稍腌拌，用冷开水冲去盐分，再与西洋芹及(B)料拌匀即可。

【Ingredients】

½ bunch celery

(A)carrot strips, ginger strips

(B) salt, monosodium glutamate, sesame oil

【Methods】

❶Cut the celery into sections, blanch them and rinse under cold water, drain.

❷Mix (A) with a pinch of salt, remove the salt in cold water, then mix well with celery and (B).

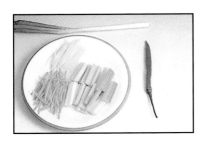

醉鸡

Wined Chicken

【材料】

鸡腿⋯⋯⋯⋯⋯⋯2 只

(A)料：葱 2 根、姜 4 片。

(B)料：绍兴酒一瓶、盐 1 小匙。

【作法】

❶ 鸡腿洗净，氽烫去血水，置碗内上铺(A)料并加 2 杯水，放入电锅蒸（锅内放 1 杯水）至开关跳起取出。

❷ 将蒸鸡之鸡汤放凉，倒入(B)料，将鸡腿放入浸泡 4 小时以上，即可剁块上桌。

【Ingredients】

2 drumsticks

(A)2 scallion, 4 slices ginger

(B)1 bottle of shao-xing wine, 1 tbsp. salt

【Methods】

❶Clean the durmsticks, blanch and put them in a bowl, spread (A) on and add 2 cups of water, steam.

❷After the juice of steamed durmsticks getting cold, mix with (B), then put the drumsticks in for 4 hours more.

糖醋鱼

【材料】
鱼……………………1 条
(A)料：酒、葱、姜、胡椒盐。
(B) 料：糖、醋、番茄酱、水
　　各 5 大匙、盐少许、水淀
　　粉适量。
(C) 料：蒜末 1 大匙，洋葱丝
　　半杯、青椒丝少许。

【作法】
❶ 鱼的全身抹上(A)料，腌20
　　分钟左右，炸时抹上蛋黄
　　及沾些淀粉于鱼身。
❷ 烧开半锅油，将整条鱼放
　　入油炸，用锅铲不断在鱼
　　身上淋油，使其定型，炸
　　至外皮酥脆即可捞出。
❸ 以 2 大匙油炒香(C)料，放
　　入(B)料烧开后再加热油 1
　　大匙（使鱼身看来更有光
　　泽），淋在鱼身上即成。

Sweet and Sour Fish

【Ingredients】
1 fish
(A)wine, scallion, ginger, pep-
　per salt
(B)sugar, vinegar, 5 tbsp.
　catsup, 5 tbsp. water, salt,
　cornstarch mixture
(C)1tbsp minced garlic, ½ cup
　onion strips, green bell
　pepper strips

【Methods】
❶ Spread (A)on the fish and
　marinate for 20 min.
❷ Heat ½ pot of oil, fry the
　fish until crisp.
❸ Fry (C) in 2 tbsp. oil till
　fragrant, add (B) and 1 tbsp.
　hot oil, then pour over the
　fish.

红烧牛腩

【材料】

牛肉⋯⋯⋯⋯⋯⋯500 克
洋葱⋯⋯⋯⋯⋯半个切丁

(A)料：胡萝卜 1 个，白萝卜半个。

(B)料：酒 1 大匙、酱油 1½ 大匙、番茄 2 个切块、盐半小匙、清水 5 杯。

【作法】

❶牛肉切块，汆烫去血水。捞出备用。

❷以 3 大匙油炒洋葱丁，加 (B)料炒匀，倒入牛肉块，烧约 20 分钟，放切块之(A)料，续烧半小时使其入味，再用少许水淀粉勾芡即可。

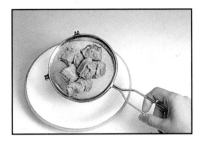

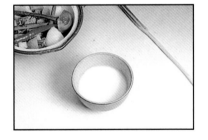

Stewed Beef

【Ingredients】

500g. beef, ½ onion (chop)

(A)1 carrot, ½ radish

(B)4 tbsp. wine, 1½ tbsp. soy sauce, 2 tomatoes, ½ tbsp salt

【Methods】

❶Cut the beef into cubes, blanch them and remove.

❷Fry chopped onion in 3 tbsp. oil, stir with (B), then put the beef in and cook for 20 min. Add (A) and stew for half an hour, thicken with cornstarch mixture.

蛤蜊丝瓜

Clam and Loofah

【材料】
澎湖丝瓜…………………2 条
蛤蜊……………………15 个
嫩姜丝…………………适量
盐…………………少许

【作法】
❶ 蛤蜊加盐，置于水中吐沙，备用。
❷ 丝瓜切轮片状，先用稍多的油氽软再取出，油滴净，备用。
❸ 留 1 大匙油，倒入蛤蜊和嫩姜，炒至蛤蜊张开即倒入丝瓜，以少许盐拌炒即可。

【Ingredients】
2 loofah, 15 clams, sliced ginger, salt

【Methods】
❶ Soak clams in salt water to remove sand out.
❷ Slice and fry the loofah.
❸ Fry sliced ginger and clams in 1 tbsp. oil till the shells of clams open. Then add loofah and a pinch of salt.

- -

九香雪螺

Fried Snail with Basil

【材料】
雪螺……………………250 克
(A) 料：葱、姜丝、蒜末适量。
(B) 料：糖、酱油、酒。
(C) 料：水淀粉、紫苏。

【作法】
❶ 用 3 大匙油将(A)料爆香，倒入雪螺拌炒，再依序加入(B)料，如太干可酌加少许热水。
❷ 以水淀粉勾芡，并加些紫苏即可盛出。

【Ingredients】
250g. snail
(A) sliced scallion, ginger, garlic
(B) sugar, soy sauce, wine
(C) cornstarch mixture, basil

【Methods】
❶ Fry (A) in 3 tbsp. oil till fragrant, then add snails, (B), and a little hot water, stir well.
❷ Thicken with cornstarch mixture and add basil.

当归虱目鱼汤

【材料】

虱目鱼⋯⋯⋯⋯⋯⋯1 条

(A)料：当归10克，枸杞子少许、姜数片。

(B)料：米酒1大匙、盐1小匙。

【作法】

鱼去鳞，鳃及鱼肚的黑膜刮除洗净，切段块状，放入炖盅中，加水6杯及(A)料，置于电饭锅中炖煮（锅内放3杯水），食用时再酌加(B)料即可。

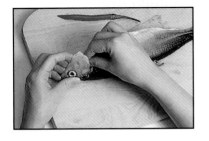

· ·

Radix Angelica Sinensis

Milk-Fish Soup

【Ingredients】

1 milk fish

(A)10g. Radix Angelica Sinensis , medlar, sliced ginger

(B)1 tbsp. rice wine, 1 tbsp. salt

【Methods】

Scrape the scales of the milkfish, remove the gill and the black of the maw. Chean it up. Cut the fish and put in a pot, add water and (A), steam it. Add (B)when serve.

47

发菜豆腐汤

【材料】
发菜……………………适量
豆腐……………………1 块
(A)料：胡萝卜丝、金针菇适
　　量。
(B)料：盐、芹菜末、香油少
　　许。高汤6杯。

【作法】
❶ 发菜洗净，沥干水分备用。
❷ 烧开6杯高汤，加入发菜
　及切小块状之豆腐，续放
　(A)料及盐，熄火后加入芹
　菜末及香油即可食用。

Laver Bean Curd Soup

【Ingredients】
laver, bean curd
(A)carrot strips, golden mushroom
(B)salt, chopped celery, sesame
oil, 6 cups of stock

【Methods】
❶Clean the laver, drain.
❷Boil 6 cups of stock, add
laver and bean curd, then
add (A) and salt. Turn off the
heat, sprinkle celery and
sesame oil.

芥兰豆皮

【材料】
芥兰菜……………250 克
炸豆腐皮……………3 片
蒜头……………2 颗拍碎
胡萝卜丝……………适量
味精、盐……………少许

【作法】
❶ 豆腐皮切长粗条，备用。
❷ 用 3 大匙油爆香蒜头，倒入芥兰菜，胡萝卜丝及豆腐皮炒匀，加入调味料即可。

Fried Chinese kale with Bean Curd

【Ingredients】
250g. Chinese kale, 3 pieces of fried bean curd, 2 garlic, carrot strips, monosodium glutamate, salt

【Methods】
❶ Slice fried bean curd by strips.
❷ Fry chopped garlic till fragrant, then add Chinese kale, carrot strips and bean curd strips, stir well and add dressing.

蒜泥白肉

【材料】
猪后腿肉………约 500 克
葱……………1 根
姜……………3 片
酒……………1 大匙
蒜泥料：蒜泥 3 大匙、酱油1 大匙、浓酱油 3 大匙、糖少许、香油1 大匙全部混合调匀。

【作法】
❶ 烧开半锅水（水量须能盖住整块肉），再放入肉块、葱、姜、酒，小火煮约 20 分钟，熄火后盖在锅里，待凉。
❷ 取出切片排于盘中，淋上调味料即可。

Minced Garlic and Sliced Pork

【Ingredients】
500g. pork, 1 scallion, 3 pieces of ginger, 1 tbsp. wine
Minced garlic sauce: blend 3 tbsp. minced garlic, 1 tbsp. soy sauce, 3 tbsp. thick soy sauce, sugar, 1 tbsp. sesame oil

【Methods】
❶ Boil the pork, add scallion, ginger and wine, then simmer in low heat for 20 min. Turn off heat, till it cool.
❷ Slice the pork and put it on a plate, then pour minced garlic sauce.

51

小鱼炒花生

Fried Little Dried Fish with Peanut

【材料】
小鱼干……………………200 克
葱………………2根（切段）
油炸花生 … … … … … 半杯
盐 … … … … … … … 少许
辣椒 … … … … … … … 少许
酱油 … … … … … … 1 大匙
酒 … … … … … … … 少许

【Ingredients】
200g. little dried fish, 2 scallion (chop), ½ cup of peanut, salt, red chili, 1 tbsp. soy sauce, wine

【作法】
❶ 小鱼用2杯热油炸至酥黄，捞出备用。
❷ 用 3 大匙油炒香葱段、辣椒，加入小鱼，淋酒及酱油拌炒均匀，起锅前再放花生米及少许盐即可。

【Methods】
❶ Fry dried fish in 2 cups of oil till golden.
❷ Fry scallion sections and red chili in 3 tbsp. oil, add little dried fish, pour wine and soy sauce in and stir well, then add peanut and a pinch of salt.

凉拌小黄瓜

Cucumber Salad

【材料】
(A).料：小黄瓜 250 克、拍碎蒜头 2 颗、盐半大匙。
(B).糖、醋各 3 大匙、辣椒少许。

【Ingredients】
(A)250g. cucumber, 2 garlic, ½ tbsp. salt
(B)sugar, vinegar, red chili

【作法】
(A) 料拌腌 20 分钟后，以冷开水略冲洗沥干，加(B)料拌匀腌 5 小时以上，待入味即可食用。

【Methods】
Mix cucumber with (A) for 20 min. rinse under cold water and drain. then mix well with (B) for 5 hour. more.

炸豆腐

Fried Bean Curd

【材料】
豆腐………………长形一块
淀粉………………………适量
调味料：酱油、糖、蒜末各适量调匀。

【Ingredients】
1 bean curd, cornstarch
Seasoning: soy sauce, sugar, chopped garlic

【作法】
❶ 豆腐切块，用餐巾纸稍吸干水分。
❷ 热2杯油，豆腐沾淀粉下锅炸至金黄即可捞出。
❸ 食用时沾调味料风味更佳。

【Methods】
❶ Slice the bean curd into cubes.
❷ Dredge each cubes of bean curd with cornstarch, fry them in 2 cups of oil till golden.
❸ Serve with the seasoning.

清蒸鲈鱼

【材料】

鲈鱼·················1 条
(A)料：葱 2 根、姜 6 片、红
辣椒 1 根均切丝。
(B)料：酒、蚝油、糖、香油、
玉米油各适量。

【作法】

❶ 鱼洗净，全身抹少许盐，
并淋上调好之(B)料，铺上
葱 1 根，姜数片，放入蒸
锅蒸约 10 数分钟后，除去
葱姜。

❷(A)料切丝泡冷开水去辛辣
味，捞出沥干水分，铺在
蒸好之鲈鱼身上，另热 3
大匙油，淋在鱼身上即可
上桌。

• •

Steamed Bass

【Ingredients】

1 Bass
(A)2 scallion, 6 slices ginger,
   1 red chili, slice all of them
   into strips
(B)wine, oyster sauce, sugar,
   sesame oil, corn oil

【Method】

❶ Clean the fish, spread a
   pinch of salt and pour (B)
   over it, then put a scallion,
   ginger slices on it, Steam
   it for 10 min. then remove
   scallion and ginger.

❷ Slice (A) into strips, soak
   them in cold water to remove spice, then drain and
   put them on the bass, after
   that, pour 3 tbsp. hot oil on
   it and enjoy.

豆豉蒸排骨

Steamed Ribs with Soy Bean

【材料】

小排骨‥‥‥‥‥‥‥‥500 克

(A)料：蒜头 3 粒、葱末 1 大匙、豆豉 1 大匙

(B)料：酒 1 大匙、酱油 1½ 大匙。糖、胡椒粉少许。

【作法】

❶ 小排骨洗净，用淀粉和酒稍腌，置于盘内。

❷ 用 3 匙油炒香(A)料，随即加入(B)料，再倒于排骨之上，放入锅里蒸约 20 分钟，可依个人喜好撒些葱花及辣椒。

【Ingredients】

500g. ribs

(A)3 garlic, 1 tbsp. chopped scallion, 1 tbsp. soy bean

(B)1 tbsp. wine, 1½ tbsp soy sauce, sugar, pepper

【Methods】

❶Clean the ribs, marinate in cornstarch and wine for minutes.

❷Fry (A) in 3 tbsp. oil till fragrant, add (B) then pour the sauce on ribs and put them in steamer for 20 min. Sprinkle chopped scallion and pepper before serving.

鱼香肉丝

Flavoured Sliced Meat

【材料】

肉丝‥‥‥‥‥‥‥‥250 克

(A)虾米 ½ 大匙、葱、姜、蒜末。木耳丝。

(B)淀粉、酱油、糖各少许。

(C)料：辣豆瓣、酒、醋、糖、盐、香油各适量。毛豆 4 汤匙。

【作法】

❶ 将肉丝拌入(B)料。

❷ 用 3 大匙油爆香(A)料，炒散肉丝，续加(C)料炒匀，以水淀粉勾芡即可。

❸ 将毛豆煮软，垫盘底，再将鱼香肉丝倒于其上即可。

【Ingredients】

250g. sliced meat:

(A)½ tbsp. dried shrimp, scallion, ginger, minced garlic, agaric

(B)cornstarch, soy sauce, sugar

(C)spicy soy bean, wine, vinegar, sugar, salt, sesame oil, 4 tbsp. bean

【Methods】

❶Mix sliced meat with (B).

❷Fry sliced meat and (A) in 3 tbsp. oil, add (C),then thicken with cornstarch mixture.

❸Cook the bean till soft, then arrange on a plate, scoop sliced meat over it and serve.

57

五福临门

【材料】

蹄筋……………………200克

豌豆荚、胡萝卜、蘑菇、木
耳各适量。

调味料：盐、味精、淡色酱
油各少许。水淀粉。

【作法】

❶ 蹄筋泡软，用姜片稍炒，
并以酱油着色，捞出备
用。

❷ 用3大匙油将四种素菜
拌炒均匀，加入1大匙高
汤及调味料，起锅前以
水淀粉勾芡即可。

Five Blessings

【Ingredients】

200g. tendon, pea pod, carrot,
mushroom, agaric
Seasoning: salt, monosodium
glutamate, soy sauce, cornstarch mixture

【Methods】

❶Soften the tendon in water,
stir well with ginger, add
soy sauce, remove.

❷Fry the vegetables, add 1
tbsp. stock and seasoning,
thicken with constarch
mixture.

猪蹄花生

【材料】
猪蹄·······················1 只
花生·················200 克
调味料：盐、味精各适量。香
菜少许、米酒数滴。

【作法】
❶ 猪蹄洗净剁块，放入滚水
中汆烫，以去除腥味。
❷ 花生用盐水浸泡1小时。
❸ 猪蹄和花生加适量清水，
大火转中火炖煮约1小
时，加调味料，食用时再
撒些香菜及米酒。

Pig's Feet with Peanut

【Ingredients】
1 Pig's funckle leg, 200g. peanut
Seasoning: salt, monosodium
glutamate, a dash of parsley
and rice wine

【Methods】
❶ Clean and chop the pig's
feet, blanch it to remove
smell.
❷ Soak peanut in salty water
for 1 hour.
❸ Add pig's feet, peanut and
water, stew in medium heat
for 1 hour, then add
seasoning, sprinkle a dash
of parsley and rice wine
before serving.

凉拌海蜇皮 Jelly-Fish Salad

【材料】
(A) 海蜇皮 200 克。
(B) 小黄瓜丝及胡萝卜丝各半杯。
(C) 料：酱油1大匙、盐、糖、香油、醋适量。蒜末1小匙。

【Ingredients】
(A)200g. jelly-fish
(B)½ cup cucumber strips, ½ cup carrot strips
(C)1 tbsp. soy sauce, salt, sugar, sesame oil, vinegar, 1 tbsp. minced garlic

【作法】
❶ 海蜇皮切丝以清水多次漂洗去盐分，用温开水氽烫后沥干水分。
❷ (B)料用少许盐抓腌片刻，用冷水冲去盐分。
❸ (C)料调匀，倒入海蜇皮及(B)料拌匀即可。

【Methods】
❶Slice jelly-fish into strips, clean and blanch in warm water, drip dry.
❷Add (B) with a dash of salt, then rinse under cold water to remove salt.
❸Add (C)、(B) and mix well.

双笋沙拉 Asparagus and Bamboo Shoots Salad

【材料】
芦笋⋯⋯⋯⋯⋯⋯⋯250 克
竹笋⋯⋯⋯⋯⋯⋯⋯ 3 只
(A)料：沙拉酱。
(B)料：酱油、香油、糖各适量混合。

【Ingredients】
250g. asparagus, 3 bamboo shoots
(A)saladdressing
(B)soy sauce, sesame oil, sugar

【作法】
❶竹笋煮熟，芦笋整枝烫熟，捞起冲冷水，竹笋切块，芦笋切段，排于盘内。
❷食用时可随意选择(A)或(B)酱淋上，冰凉后风味更佳。

【Methods】
❶Boil bamboo shoots till well-done, blanch asparagus, chop bamboo shoots, cut asparagus into sections, then arrange them on a plate.
❷Choose dressing (A) or (B) when serve.

什锦煲

【材料】
高汤……………半砂锅
豆腐……………长形一块
香菇、大白菜、蛋饺、肉片、
鱼板、虾子、青菜……（材
料可依个人喜好自由选择）。

【作法】
在空砂锅里先放入较耐煮的
材料，肉片可先以葱姜蒜拌
炒，调上酱油、糖后再放入
砂锅内。注入高汤，等汤煮
沸，再放入青菜类，即可上
桌享用。

Assorted Stew

【Ingredients】
½ clay pot stock, 1 bean curd,
Chinese mushroom, cabbage,
egg dumpling, sliced meat,
fish cake, green vegetable
(anything you like)

【Methods】
Put some ingredients that can
cook longer in a clay pot and
cook them, fry sliced meat
with scallion, ginger and
garlic, add a dash of soy
sauce, sugar, and pour stock
in. After boiling, add vegetables and serve.

银鱼苋菜羹

【材料】

银鱼……………200克
苋菜……………适量
(A)料：香菇丝，胡萝卜丝各
2大匙。
(B)料：葱2根、姜3片
(C)料：高汤、酒、盐各适量。
胡椒粉、香油少许。水淀
粉少许。

【作法】

❶ 银鱼在滚水中余烫捞出
备用。
❷ 用2大匙油将(B)料爆炒后
捞除，续放(A)料拌炒，再
放入(C)料。
❸ 水开后，以水淀粉勾芡，
倒入银鱼及苋菜，食用时
撒胡椒粉及滴少许香油即
可。

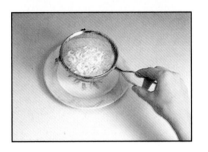

Silverfish and Amaranth in Thick Soup

【Ingredients】

200g. silverfish, amaranth.
(A)Chinese mushroom and
carrot strips
(B)2 scallion, 3 slices ginger
(C)stock, wine, salt, pepper,
sesame oil, cornstarch mixture

【Methods】

❶Blanch the silverfish.
❷Fry (B) in 2 tbsp. oil till
fragrant and remove. Add
(A) and (C), stir well.
❸After the soup being boiling,
add silverfish and amaranth,
sprinkle a dash of pepper
and sesame oil before
serving.

柠檬鸡

【材料】

鸡胸肉……………2 片

(A)料：酒、酱油各1大匙。

(B)料：蛋白½个、淀粉适量。

(C)料：番茄酱、糖各半大匙、盐少许、高汤半杯、香油、胡椒粉、水淀粉各适量，柠檬半个，香菜屑少许。

【作法】

❶ 鸡胸肉切片加(A)料，腌20分钟后沾(B)料（依序），下油锅炸成金黄色再盛出。

❷ 半个量之柠檬汁和(C)料混合煮沸后，淋于鸡肉上即可。

• •

Lemon Chicken

【Ingredients】

2 slices chicken breast

(A)1 tbsp. wine, 1 tbsp. soy sauce

(B)½ egg white, cornstarch

(C)½ tbsp. catsup, ½ tbsp. sugar, salt, ½ lemon, minced parsley

【Methods】

❶Slice the chicken and add (A) marinate for 20 min. then dip (B), fry in hot oil till golden.

❷Mix lemon juice with (C), then pour on the chicken.

洋葱肉丝

【材料】
洋葱……………一个切丝
肉丝……………300 克
青葱……………2 根切段
(A)料：酱油、酒、淀粉。
(B)料：盐、酱油、糖适量。白
　　　芝麻少许。

【作法】
❶ 肉丝加入(A)料拌匀，腌10
　分钟备用。
❷ 用3匙油炒散肉丝，续放
　入洋葱丝及葱段拌炒。
❸ 加入(B)料拌炒，撒些白芝
　麻即可盛出。

Fry Onion with Sliced Meat

【Ingredients】
1 onion, 300g. sliced meat, 2 scallion
(A)Soy sauce, wine, cornstarch
(B)salt, soy sauce, sugar, sesame seed

【Methods】
❶ Mix sliced meat with (A) for 10 min.
❷ Fry sliced meat in 3 tbsp. oil, add onion strips and chopped scallion.
❸ Add (B) and sprinkle sesame seed.

双蔬鸡丝

【材料】
冷冻毛豆……………半杯
雪里红…………切碎2 杯
鸡胸肉………切丝300 克
拍碎蒜头……………2 颗
(A)料：淀粉、盐、酒少许。
(B)味精、盐少许。

【作法】
用3大匙油炒香蒜头，倒入拌上(A)料的肉丝，略炒后加入雪里红，毛豆及(B)料，拌炒均匀即可。

Fry Sliced Chicken with Bean and Potherb mustard

【Ingredients】
½ cup frozen bean, 2 cup chopped Potherb mustard, 300g. sliced chicken, 2 garlic
(A)cornstarch, salt, wine
(B)monosodium glutamate, salt

【Methods】
Fry minced garlic in 3 tbsp. oil till fragrant, add sliced chicken and (A) stir well. Then add Potherb mustard, bean and (B), fry well.

71

枸杞参鸡汤

【材料】

鸡 … … … … … … … 半 只

(A)料：枸杞子1大匙、参须3条。

(B)料：姜片3片。盐少许。

【作法】

❶ 鸡剁块用开水烫去血水，洗净备用。

❷ 鸡块放入锅中，注入8杯水及(A),(B)料，大火改小火慢煮约40分钟，加入少许盐即可。

- -

Wolfberry, Ginseng and Chicken Soup

【Ingredients】

½ chicken

(A)1 tbsp. Fruit of Chinese Wolfberry, 3 Ginseng

(B)3 slices ginger, salt

【Methods】

❶Chop and blanch the chiken.

❷Put the chicken in a pot, put in 8 cups of water and add (A), (B), then cook in medium heat for 40 min. and add a pinch of salt.

黑胡椒牛柳

【材料】

里脊牛肉…………250克
蒜末………………半大匙
洋葱……………… 1 个
蘑菇片………………适量
(A)料：酒1大匙、酱油1大
　　　匙、糖、淀粉少许。
(B)料：黑胡椒粉1大匙、香
　　　油、酱油适量。

【作法】

❶ 牛肉切粗条，拌入(A)料腌
　 20分钟。
❷ 用5大匙油爆香蒜末，加
　 入牛肉拌炒，捞出备用。
❸ 留油2大 匙，炒洋葱丝和
　 蘑菇，倒入牛肉条及(B)料
　 快速拌炒即可盛出。

● ●

Black Pepper Beef

【Ingredients】

250g. beef,
½ tbsp. minced garlic, 1 onion,
mushroom slices
(A)1 tbsp. wine, 1 tbsp. soy
　　sauce, sugar, cornstarch
(B)1 tbsp. black pepper
　　powder, sesame oil, soy
　　sauce

【Methods】

❶Slice the beef, mix with (A)
　for 20 min.
❷Fry chopped garlic in 2 tbsp.
　oil, stir well with the beef,
　remove.
❸Remain 2 tbsp. oil to fry
　onion and mushroom
　strips, add beef slices and
　(B), stir well and serve.

家常豆腐

【材料】

豆腐 ………………… 2 块
(A)料：木耳丝、葱段、胡萝卜丝、豌豆荚各适量。
(B)料：酱油、酒、糖各适量。水淀粉少量。

【作法】

❶ 将豆腐切成三角形或块状，下油锅炸至表面金黄。
❷ 用2匙油炒(A)料，放入炸好之豆腐，续放(B)料，小火焖煮入味，最后再以水淀粉勾芡即可。

Ordinary Plain Bean Curd

【Ingredients】

2 bean curd
(A)agaric strips, scallion sections, carrot strips, peas
(B)soy sauce, wine, sugar, cornstarch mixture

【Methods】

❶Cut bean curd into triangle lumps.
❷Fry (A) in 2 tbsp. oil, add the fried bean curd and (B), then cook under low heat for minutes. Thicken with cornstarch mixture.

- -

香辣海瓜子

【材料】

海瓜子………………500 克
紫苏 ………………… 适 量
(A)料：拍碎大蒜5颗、辣椒2根、姜丝、葱花各一大匙。
(B)酒1大匙、酱油3大匙，糖，胡椒粉各少许。

【作法】

❶ 用3大匙油将(A)料爆香，倒入海瓜子拌炒，加入(B)料。
❷ 等海瓜子一张开，续放紫苏快速拌炒，即可盛出。

Spicy Clams

【Ingredients】

500g. clams, basil
(A)5 garlic, 2 red chili, ginger strips, chopped scallion
(B)1 tbsp. wine, 3 tbsp. soy sauce, sugar, a pinch of pepper

【Methods】

❶ Fry (A) in 3 tbsp. oil till fragrant, then add clam and (B), stir well.
❷When clams shells start to open, add basil and stir.

竹笋鸡汤

【材料】

鸡 腿 …………………… 2	只
笋 干 …………………… 6~7	条
香 菇 …………………… 6	朵
姜 ……………………… 数	片
酒 ……………………… 少	许
盐 ……………………… 适	量

【作法】

❶ 鸡切块，用开水烫去血水，笋干、香菇用水泡软备用。

❷ 洗净鸡块加入开水6杯，水滚加入竹笋（切段）、香菇（对切）、姜、酒后，转小火慢煮至鸡腿肉软，加盐调味，即可盛出食用。

- -

Bamboo Fungus & Chicken Soup

【Ingredients】

2 drumsticks. 6~7 bamboo pit, 6 Chinese mushroom, sliced ginger, wine, salt

【Methods】

❶Chop the chicken into cubes and blanch them. Soften the bamboo fungus and mushroom.

❷Clean the chicken cubes, add 6 cups of water and bring to boil, then add chopped bamboo fungus, mushroom, ginger and wine, after that, turn down the heat and cook till the chicken get soft. Sprinkle a dash of salt and serve.

中式猪排

【材料】

里脊肉⋯⋯⋯⋯⋯⋯⋯8 片
洋葱⋯⋯⋯⋯⋯1个（切丝）

(A)料：酱油、酒、糖、蒜末、水淀粉各适量。

(B)料：番茄酱、酱油、糖、水、陈醋各适量。白芝麻少许。

【作法】

❶ 里脊肉去白筋，用刀拍松，调入(A)料拌匀，腌约半小时。

❷ 热油，将里脊肉片煎至两面金黄，捞出备用。

❸ 用3大匙油将洋葱丝炒香，加入(B)料及煎好的肉片拌匀，用大火将汁烧到 快干时，淋上热油即可盛盘，上面可撒些芝麻。

• •

Fried Pork

【Ingredients】

Pork (slice into pieces), 1 on-ion (slice into strips)

(A)soy sauce, wine, sugar, chopped garlic, cornstarch mixture

(B)catsup, soy sauce, sugar, water, black vinegar, white sesame seeds

【Methods】

❶ Mix pork with (A) for half an hour.

❷ Heat oil, fry the pork till both side golden, remove.

❸ Fry onion strips in 3 tbsp. oil, add (B) and fried pork, stir well. Cook in high heat till the juice almost dry, pour hot oil over and sprinkle white sesame seeds.

翠玉虾仁

【材料】

煮熟毛豆……………半杯
虾仁………………250 克
(A)料：葱1根切段、姜2片。
(B)料：盐少许、蛋白半个、淀
　　　粉1小匙。
(C)料：盐、酒少许。

【作法】

❶ 虾仁去肠泥，洗净并擦干
　水分，拌入(B)料，腌片刻。
❷ 将足量的油烧至七、八分
　热，倒入虾仁过油，待虾
　变色即捞出。
❸ 留2大匙油炒香(A)料，再
　倒入虾仁，加入(C)料拌炒
　即可。

Fried with Green Peas Shrimp

【Ingredients】

½ cup well-done peas
250g. shrimp
(A)1 scallion, 2 slices ginger
(B)salt, ½ egg white, 1 tbsp. cornstarch
(C)salt, wine

【Methods】

❶ Clean the shrimp and re-move tendon from stomach, then mix with (B) for minutes.
❷ Run shrimp through me-dium heat oil, remove when shrimp change color.
❸ Fry (A) in 2 tbsp. oil, add shrimp and (C), stir well and enjoy.

凉拌鸡丝

【材料】

鸡胸……………………1 个
胡萝卜丝、芹菜切段、石花
菜、豆腐干5片切丝。
调味料：姜丝、酱油2大匙、
糖、醋各少许、香油1大匙、
蒜末、辣椒可依个人喜爱增
减。

【作法】

❶ 鸡胸烫熟，撕成条状，胡
　萝卜、芹菜用开水稍烫，
　石花菜用温水泡软切段，
　豆腐干烫熟切丝备用。
❷ 调味料拌匀后，倒入所有
　材料里，加入香菜即可食
　用。

Chicken Strips Salad

【Ingredients】

1 chicken breast, carrots strips, celery sections, agar, 5 bean curd (blanch and strip)
Seasoning: ginger strips, 2 tbsp. soy sauce, sugar, vinegar, 1 tbsp. sesame oil, chopped garlic, chili pepper

【Methods】

❶ Blanch the chicken breast, carrot, celery and tear the chicken into strips. Put the agar in warm water, then cut it into sections after being soften.
❷ Mix the seasoning well, put all the ingredients in and add parsley.

烤鸡

【材料】

鸡……………………1 只
调味料：酒1大匙、酱油2大
匙、糖2大匙、辣椒酱2大匙。

【作法】

❶ 鸡洗净，用叉子在鸡身均
匀扎洞，再以调味料腌约
20分钟，中间可多次用刷
子沾调味料抹鸡身。

❷ 烤箱先预热，再以250度
火力烤，中途须注意火
力，并应将调味料反覆涂
于鸡身，烤约20分钟即
可。

Baked Chicken

【Ingredients】

1 chicken
seasoning: 1 tbsp. wine, 2
tbsp. soy sauce, 2 tbsp. sugar,
2 tbsp. chili sauce

【Methods】

❶ Clean the chicken and jab
by fork, then marinate with
seasoning for 20 min.

❷ Warm the oven, then bake
the chicken in 250 degree.
Watch out the heat and
brush the seasoning on the
chicken repeatedly when it
is baking. Bake it for 20
min. and enjoy.

菠萝鸡丁

【材料】

鸡腿肉·················1 只
菠萝（罐头）··········三片
(A)料：酱油、酒、水淀粉、糖
　各少许。
(B)料：葱2根切段、姜数片，
　青椒一个切块。

【作法】

❶ 鸡腿去骨，筋稍切断，肉
　拍松，切丁腌(A)料。
❷ 热5大匙油，将鸡肉过油
　捞出备用。
❸ 留油2大匙，炒香葱、姜，
　加入菠萝块及青椒，再将
　鸡丁倒入拌炒，淋上综合
　调味汁（酱油、酒、糖、水
　淀粉各适量）即可。

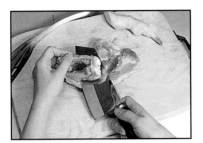

Diced Chicken with Pineapple

【Ingredients】

1 drumstick remove the bone,
1 pineapple can
(A)soy sauce, wine, cornstarch
　mixture, sugar
(B)2 scallion, sliced ginger,
　green bell pepper cubes

【Methods】

❶Cut the chicken into cubes,
　mix with (A).
❷Run through the chicken in
　5 tbsp. hot oil.
❸Fry scallion sections, gin-
　ger slices, pineapple and
　green bell pepper in 2 tbsp.
　oil, then add the chicken,
　stir and fry well, pour (A) on
　and serve.

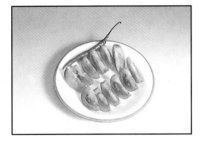

番茄炒蛋

【材料】

番茄 …………………… 2 个
蛋 ……………………… 4 个
葱 ……………………… 2 根
番茄酱 ………………… 1 大匙
糖、盐 ………………… 少许

【作法】

❶ 番茄切片，蛋打散，葱切段备用。

❷ 用 3 大匙油将蛋炒散，凝固成块状续放葱段及番茄片拌炒，加入番茄酱等调味料，如太干可加些水炒匀即可。

Fied Tomato with Egg

【Ingredients】

2 tomatoes, 4 eggs, 2 scallion, 1 tbsp. catsup, sugar, salt

【Methods】

❶ Slice the tomatoes, beat the eggs, chop scallion into sections.

❷ Scramble the beaten eggs, as soon as the egg mixture starts to thick, add scallion, tomato slices, catsup and seasoning.

香卤肥肠

【材料】

大肠头 ………………… 3~4 条
葱 ……………………… 2 根
姜 ……………………… 3 片
香菜 …………………… 少许
调味料：酒 1 大匙、酱油 2 大匙、盐少许、清水 3 杯、糖适量。

【作法】

❶ 大肠头清洗干净（可买已处理好的大肠头）。

❷ 加入葱、姜、酒煮约 30 分钟，去腥煮软。

❸ 大肠头取出切段，加入所有调味料同煮，待汤汁收干时即可盛出。

Stewed Pork's Large Intestine

【Ingredients】

3~4 intestine, 2 scallion, 3 slices ginger, parsley
Seasoning: 1 tbsp. wine, 2 tbsp. soy sauce, salt, 3 cups of water, sugar

【Methods】

❶ Clean the intestine.

❷ Add scallion, ginger, wine and cook for 30 min. till soft.

❸ Chop the intestine into sections, add the seasoning and cook till the gravy is almost dry.

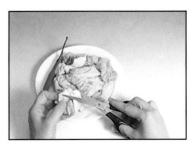

笋菇肉丸汤

【材料】

(A)料：竹笋 2 支、香菇 6 朵（切丝）。

(B)料：猪肉馅 300 克、葱屑、姜末、胡椒粉、淀粉少许。

(C)料：芹菜末、油炸过的洋葱末少许。高汤 8 杯、盐、味精少许。

【作法】

❶ 将(B)料充分拌匀，甩打数下做成肉丸。

❷ 8 杯高汤加入(A)料烧开，再将肉丸一个个的放入高汤中，待汤再滚时熄火，撒下(C)料即可。

Bamboo Shoot and Meat Balls Soup

【Ingredients】

(A) 2 bamboo shoot, 6 Chinese mushroom slice into strips

(B) 300g. minced meat, chopped scallion, ginger, pepper, cornstarch

(C) chopped celery, fried chopped onion, 8 cups of stock, salt, monosodium glutamate

【Methods】

❶ Mix (B) well, beat and make into meat balls.

❷ Mix 8 cups of stock with (A), when the soup is boiling. Put meat balls in the soup one by one, after the soup is boiling again, sprinkle (C) and serve.

烩素菜

【材料】

青花椰菜、玉米笋、草菇、胡萝卜片、木耳丝各适量。

调味料：高汤半杯、盐、味精、水淀粉各少许。

【作法】

❶ 青花椰菜（清洗切适量大小），玉米笋（对半切），胡萝卜片先在加盐之水中氽烫。

❷ 用 3 大匙油拌炒所有蔬菜，淋上调味料即可盛出。

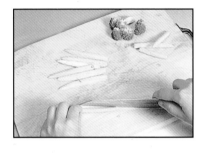

Braised Assorted Vegetables

【Ingredients】

Green cauliflower, little corn, mushroom, sliced carrot, agaric strips

seasoning:½ cup stock, salt, monosodium glutamate, corn-starch mixture

【Methods】

❶Clean the green cauliflower and cut them up, cut little corn vertically, slice carrot and blanch them in hot salt water.

❷Fry all the vegetables in 3 tbsp. oil, pour the seasoning on them and serve.

烤三菇

【材料】
(A)料：香菇、金针菇、口蘑各适量。
(B)料：葱段、胡萝卜丝、椒盐、奶油各适量。

【作法】
❶ 将香菇和口蘑的菇面用刀划上交叉两刀，金针菇切段。
❷ 处理好之三菇放在锡箔纸上，再加入(B)料，锡箔纸包妥，放入小烤箱烤约7-8分钟后，即可取出食用。

Baked 3 Mushroom

【Ingredients】
(A)Chinese mushroom, gold mushroom, mushroom
(B)scallion sections, carrot strips, pepper salt, butter

【Methods】
❶Slash Chinese mushroom and mushroom intersection on surface.
❷Put 3 kinds of mushroom on tinfoil, add (B), wrap and bake for 7~8 min.

红油抄手

【材料】
(A)料：肉馅400克，葱姜2大匙、盐、胡椒粉少许。
(B)料：红油 1½ 大匙、酱油、糖、葱花、蒜泥、陈醋各适量。
馄饨皮……………………200 克
香 菜…… …… …… …… 少 许

【作法】
❶ (A)料加少许水调匀，再以馄饨皮包，即为抄手。
❷ (B)料调匀，分量可依个人口味增减。
❸ 水烧开，放入抄手，待水滚抄手浮起即可捞出，食用时，和放于碗内的(B)料拌匀。

Meat Dumpling in Chili Oil

【Ingredients】
(A)400g. minced meat, 2 tbsp. chopped scallion and ginger, salt, pepper
(B)1½ tbsp. chili oil, soy sauce, sugar, chopped scallion, mash garlic, black vinegar. 200g. dumpling skin, parsley

【Methods】
❶Mix (A) with some water, wrap in dumpling skin and fold into a shape of dumpling.
❷Mix (B) well.
❸Cook dumpling in boiling water till float. Put the dumpling in a bowl and mix well with (B).

三杯小卷

【材料】
墨斗鱼⋯⋯⋯⋯⋯⋯250克
(A)料：姜数片、辣椒2根、大蒜4颗。
(B)料：米酒、酱油、黑芝麻油各4大匙。紫苏适量。

【作法】
❶ 墨斗鱼洗净，切段后放入开水中稍烫，捞出备用。
❷ 热黑芝麻油，爆香(A)料，再放入墨斗鱼，加入(B)料拌炒，以小火烧到汁稍收干，加入紫苏拌匀即可。

Clay Pot Cuttlefish

【Ingredients】
250g. cuttlefish
(A)ginger slices, 2 chili, 4 garlic
(B)rice wine, soy sauce, 4 tbsp. balck sesame oil, basil

【Methods】
❶ Clean the cuttlefish and slice into sections, blanch them in hot water.
❷ Fry (A) in 3 tbsp. black sesame oil till fragrant, add cuttlefish and (B), stir and fry well, cook under low heat till the juice almost dry, then add basil.

蜜汁火腿

【材料】

火腿……………500克
土司面包……………半条
(A)料：黄砂糖5大匙、酒2大
　　匙。
(B)料：淀粉、水各少许。

【作法】

❶ 火腿外皮刷洗干净，在水里煮30分钟至熟，捞起。待凉切长薄片，排在盘内，将(A)料铺在火腿上蒸2小时。

❷ 蒸火腿释出之汤汁（约1杯量）如太干，可加些水再以水淀粉勾芡，淋于火腿上。

❸ 土司放冰箱冰硬，再切成活页状，用以夹食蜜汁火腿。

Honey Ham

【Ingredients】

500g. ham, ½ loaf toast
(A)5 tbsp. sugar, 2 tbsp. wine
(B)cornstarch, water

【Methods】

❶Clean the ham, boil it for 30 min. remove. Slice it into rectangles after it getting cold, arrange them in a plate, pour (A) on the ham and steam for 2 hours.

❷Thicken the juice of steamed ham with cornstarch, pour it over the ham.

❸Slice each piece of bread horizontally through ⅔ of the way, sandwich with steamed ham.

炸春卷

【材料】
韭菜、肉丝、香菇丝各适量。春卷皮10张。盐、味精少许。

【作法】
① 肉丝拌酱油、淀粉腌约10分钟，起油锅炒散，加入香菇丝及、韭菜段稍炒马上盛出。
② 桌上摊开春卷皮，将炒好之材料包成条状，封口以面粉糊粘合即可。
③ 热4杯油，再一一放入春卷油炸，因里面材料已熟，因此表面稍炸成金黄色即可捞出。

Fried Spring Roll

【Ingredients】
Leek, sliced meat, Chinese mushroom strips, 10 thin cakes, salt, monosodium glutamate

【Methods】
❶ Mix sliced meat with soy sauce and cornstarch for 10 min. Fry them well, add Chinese mushroom strips and leek sections.
❷ Roll the stuff with thin cakes.
❸ Heat 4 cups of oil, fry the rolls till golden.

荫豉蚝

【材料】
生蚝……………250克
水淀粉、蒜苗少许。
(A)料：葱、姜、蒜末各半大匙、豆豉2大匙。
(B)料：酱油3大匙、糖少许。

【作法】
❶ 生蚝洗净，以开水氽烫，捞出备用。
❷ 热油3大匙，爆香(A)料，加入蚝及(B)料，以水淀粉勾芡，撒上蒜苗即可盛盘。

Fried Soy Bean with Oyster

【Ingredients】
250g. oyster
cornstarch mixture, garlic sprouts
(A)½ tbsp. chopped scallion, ginger and garlic, 2 tbsp. soy bean
(B)3 tbsp. soy sauce, sugar

【Methods】
❶ Clean and blanch the oyster.
❷ Fry (A) in 3 tbsp. oil till fragrant, add oyster and (B), then thicken with cornstarch mixture, sprinkle garlic sprouts.

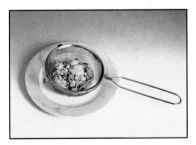

葱爆虾

【材料】

虾……………………２５０克

(A)料：葱段、姜片、辣椒适
量。

(B)料：酒、酱油、糖适量。

【作法】

❶ 虾洗净、剪去须足，洗净
肠泥。

❷ 热3大匙油，倒入(A)料及
虾快炒，续加入(B)料炒
匀，即可熄火盛出。

Sauted Shrimp with Scallion

【Ingredients】

250g. shrimp

(A)scallion sections, sliced
ginger, chili

(B)wine, soy sauce, sugar

【Methods】

❶ Clean the shrimp and remove tendon from
stomach.

❷ Heat 3 tbsp. oil, add (A) and
shrimp, fry guickly, then
add (B).

103

鳕鱼豆腐

【材料】

鳕鱼⋯⋯⋯⋯⋯⋯1 大片

盒装豆腐⋯⋯⋯⋯⋯⋯1 盒

(A)料：葱段、姜片、酒、盐
  适量。

(B)料：酱油4大匙，糖、醋、
  香油、胡椒粉各适量。

(C)料：花椒粒、葱、姜、大
  蒜末各1大匙，芹菜、香
  菜少许。

【作法】

❶ 鳕鱼洗净，抹酒、盐，铺
  上(A)料中之葱、姜，入蒸
  锅蒸熟，待凉用筷子将鱼
  挟成块状。

❷ 豆腐切块，倒入鱼块里。

❸ 花椒粒用2大匙油炒香后
  捞除，续放(B)料烧开，汁
  淋在鱼和豆腐上，撒下芹
  菜末及香菜即可。

• •

Cod and Bean Curd

【Ingredients】

1 slice cod, 1 bean curd

(A)scallion sections, sliced
  ginger, wine, salt

(B)4 tbsp. soy sauce, sugar,
  vinegar, sesame oil,
  pepper

(C)xanthoxylon seeds,
  chopped scallion, ginger,
  garlic, celery, parsley

【Methods】

❶Clean the cod, spread wine
  and salt over it then put (A)
  on and steam. Cut the cod
  into cubes after it getting
  cold.

❷Cut the bean curd, mix with
  the cod.

❸Fry xanthoxylon seeds in 2
  tbsp. oil till fragrant,
  remove, add (B) and cook,
  pour the sauce on the cod
  and bean curd, sprinkle
  chopped celery and
  parsley.

姜丝鸡

【材料】
鸡……半只（或鸡腿两只）
姜 丝 ……………… 半 杯
酒 ……………… 1 大匙
酱油 ……………… 3 大匙
糖 ……………… 半大匙

【作法】
❶ 鸡切块，用滚水烫去血水，洗净备用。
❷ 用3大匙油爆香姜丝，再倒入鸡块、酱油、酒、糖同炒。
❸ 待鸡块炒至表面熟时，大火转小火焖烧约20分钟，即可盛出。

Ginger Strips Chicken

【Ingredients】
½ chicken (or 2 drumsticks), ½ cup ginger strips, 1 tbsp. wine, 3 tbsp. soy sauce, ½ tbsp. sugar

【Methods】
❶Chop the chicken into cubes, blanch and clean them.
❷Fry ginger strips in 3 tbsp. oil till fragrant, then add chicken cubes, soy sauce, wine, sugar, fry well.
❸fry till the chicken almost well-done, turn down the heat and simmer for 20 min.

炒海茸

【材料】
海茸………………300 克
肉馅……………… 适量
(A)料：葱段、姜丝、蒜末适量。
(B)料：酱油半大匙、酒、醋、糖、盐各适量。胡萝卜丝、辣椒丝各少许。

【作法】
❶ 海茸放入滚水中煮软，捞出沥干备用。
❷ 用2大匙油炒香(A)料，倒入海茸续炒。
❸ (B)料在碗中调和，再倒入作法❷同炒，起锅前撒下胡萝卜丝和辣椒丝炒匀，即可盛出。

Fried Spiral Sea-weed

【Ingredients】
300g. spiral seaweed, minced meat
(A)scallion sections, ginger strips, chopped garlic
(B)½ tbsp. soy sauce, wine, vinegar, sugar, salt, carrot strips, chili strips

【Methods】
❶Soften the spiral seaweed, drain.
❷ Fry (A) in 2 tbsp. oil till fragrant, add spiral seaweed, stir.
❸Mix (B) well in a bowl, then pour in ❷ and fry. Before scooping out, sprinkle carrot strips and chili strips.

翡翠白玉

【材料】

鸡胸肉………………一块
绿豆芽………………250 克
油菜………………6 棵
(A)料：盐、酒、淀粉适量。
(B)料：盐、味精少许。

【作法】

❶ 鸡胸肉切丝，拌入(A)料约 20 分钟。

❷ 绿豆芽摘去头尾，油菜对切备用。

❸ 用 3 大匙油将肉丝炒散，倒入豆芽菜及(B)料拌匀后即可盛出。

❹ 将对切之油菜放入开水中汆烫，捞出拌少许盐和油，置于豆芽肉丝外围即可。

Chicken Strips and Green Vegetables

【Ingredients】

1 chicken breast, 250g. bean sprouts, 6 green cabbage
(A)salt, wine, cornstarch
(B)salt, monosodium gluta-mate

【Methods】

❶Slice the chicken into strips, mix with (A) for 20 min.

❷Remove the head and toe of bean sprouts, cut green cabbage vertically.

❸fry the chicken in 3 tbsp. oil, add bean sprouts and (B), stir well then remove to a plate.

❹Blanch the green cabbage, mix with a dash of salt and oil and arrange around the chicken.

玉米肉丸

【材料】

肉馅……………………250克
玉米粒……………………1 杯
(A)料：葱姜蒜末、盐、胡椒
　　粉、淀粉各适量。
(B)料：高汤半杯、酱油1小
　　匙、盐、糖、香油、淀粉
　　各适量。

【作法】

❶ 将肉馅剁碎，和(A)料充分
　拌匀，甩打后做成数个肉
　丸，放入蒸锅蒸熟。
❷ 盘底倒入煮熟之玉米粒，
　再将肉丸排在玉米粒上。
❸ 将(B)料煮开，淋在作法 ❷
　上即可上桌。

• •

Corn Meat Balls

【Ingredients】

250g. minced meat, 1 cup of
corn beads
(A)chopped scallion, ginger,
　garlic, salt, pepper, corn-
　starch
(B)½ cup stock, 1 tbsp. soy
　sauce, salt, sugar, sesame
　oil, cornstarch

【Methods】

❶Chop the minced meat, mix
　well with (A), beat it and
　make into balls then steam.
❷ Put the corn beads on a
　plate, arrange the meat
　balls on them.
❸Boil (B), pour over method
　❷ and enjoy.

什锦汤面

【材料】
面条 …………………… 适量
高汤 …………………… 2 碗
小里脊肉片……………适量
(A)料：鱼板、虾、青菜、胡
　　萝卜丝适量。
(B)料：盐、香油少许。

【作法】
❶ 面条以开水氽烫，去碱
　味，冲水备用。
❷ 虾氽烫，捞出备用。小里
　脊切片拌少许酱油、酒、
　淀粉备用。
❸ 锅内煮开高汤下面，里脊
　肉一片片加入，汤滚再加
　入其他材料即可盛出食
　用。

Assorted Noodle

【Ingredients】
Glossy noodle, 2 bowls stock,
sliced meat
(A)fish cake, shrimp, vegetable,
　carrot strips
(B)salt, sesame oil

【Methods】
❶ Blanch the noodle, rinse
　under cold water.
❷ Blanch the shrimp. Mix the
　sliced meat with soy sauce,
　wine, cornstarch.
❸ Boil the stock, add noodle
　and meat, when the soup is
　boiling, add the rest of
　ingredients.

美味炒米粉

【材料】
米 粉 ………………… 半 包
肉 丝 ………………… 适 量
(A)料：香菇、虾米适量。
(B)料：圆白菜丝、胡萝卜丝。
(C)料：酱油、盐各适量。蒜
　末、芹菜末、胡椒粉各适
　量。

【作法】
❶ 香菇、虾米用水泡软后香
　菇切丝，米粉用清水泡
　软，沥干水分后备用。
❷ 用3大匙油炒香(A)料，加
　入肉丝拌炒，续加(B)料同
　炒，倒入(C)料及半杯清
　水，汤汁稍滚放入米粉拌
　炒，起锅时撒下蒜末、芹
　菜末、胡椒粉更觉美味。

Fried Rice Noodle

【Ingredients】
½ pack rice noodle, sliced
meat
(A)Chinese mushroom, dried
　shrimp
(B)cabbage strips, carrot
　strips
(C)soy sauce, salt, chopped
　garlic, celery, pepper

【Methods】
❶ Soften the mushroom and
　dried shrimp. Slice the
　mushroom into strips. Soak
　the rice noodle in water to
　be soften, then drain.
❷ Fry (A) in 3 tbsp. oil, add
　sliced meat and (B), fry well.
　Add (C) and ½ cup of water,

when the soup almost boil,
add rice noodle. Sprinkle
chopped garlic, celery and
pepper before scooping
out.

113

烩海参

【材料】

海参 … … … … … … … 2　条
(A)料：笋片、胡萝卜片。
(B)料：油菜、香菇各适量。
(C)料：酱油、酒、醋、蚝油、
　　盐、糖各适量。水淀粉。

【作法】

❶ 海参洗净肠泥、切粗条
　状。
❷ 起油锅爆香姜片，倒入海
　参同炒，续加酱油、酒焖
　煮至软，海参煮至软，海
　参捞出备用，汤汁倒除。
❸ (A)料用开水煮熟、香菇泡
　软切丝备用。
❹ 起油锅爆香葱段，加入(A)
　料，香菇及海参同炒，再
　加入油菜快速拌炒，淋上
　调和之(C)料勾芡即可。

Braised Trepang

【Ingredients】

2 trepang
(A)sliced bamboo shoot, carrot
(B)green cabbage, Chinese
mushroom
(C)soy sauce, wine, vinegar,
oyster oil, salt, sugar

【Methods】

❶Clean the trepang and slice
into long strips.
❷ Fry sliced ginger till
fragrant, add trepang and
stir and fry, add soy sauce
and wine then braise till
soft.
❸Cook (A), soften mushroom
and slice into strips.
❹Fry scallion sections till
fragrant, add (A), mush-
room and trepang, then add
green cabbage, stir and fry
quickly, pour (C) on them
and thicken with cornstarch
mixture.

虾仁肠粉

【材料】

虾仁………………………适量

河粉………………………3张

葱、香菜………………各少许

(A)料：蛋白½、盐、胡椒粉、
淀粉各少许。

(B)料：蚝油4大匙，高汤1杯、
糖适量、水淀粉1大匙，胡
椒粉、香油少许。

【作法】

❶ 虾仁去肠泥洗净，拭干水
分，拌入(A)料稍腌。

❷ 河粉切成约20公分长10
公分宽之尺寸，摊开河
粉，铺上虾仁适量。

❸ 将铺上虾仁之河粉卷成
长条状，置于已抹少许油
之盘内，放入蒸锅蒸熟即
可取出。

❹ 将(B)料调和并在锅中煮
开，淋在蒸好之河粉上，
撒少许葱花及香菜屑即可
食用。

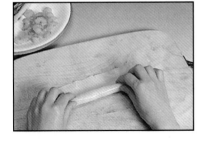

Steamed Shrimp Rolls

【Ingredients】

Shrimp, 3 sheets of thin rice
cake, scallion, parsley

(A)½ egg white, salt, pepper,
cornstarch

(B)4 tbsp. oyster oil, 1 cup of
stock, sugar, 1 tbsp. cornstarch mixture

【Methods】

❶Clean the shrimp and re-
move the tendon from
stomach. mix with (A).

❷Slice the thin rice cake into
20x10cm, spread shrimp
on each one.

❸Roll them into long shape,
place on a plate which
spreaded some oil on and
steam.

❹Mix and boil (B), pour the
seasoning on the steamed
rolls and sprinkle a dash of
chopped scallion, parsley.

圆白菜饼

Cabbage Pan Cake

【材料】

(A)料：圆白菜切丁1杯、低筋面粉2汤匙、蛋1个、盐、味精、水少许。

(B)料：青海苔、咸鱼末、肉2片、陈醋少许。

【Ingredients】

(A)1 cup of cabbage cubes, 2 tbsp. cake flour, 1 egg, salt, monosodium glutamate, water

(B)green laver, stock fish, 2 slices of meat, black vinegar

【作法】

❶ 将(A)料全部拌匀。

❷ 平底锅里以2大匙油抹匀，待七、八分热时，将拌好之(A)料倒入锅内煎，并用铲子整型成圆饼状（稍压平），铺上两片肉后，再翻面煎（火不宜太大）。

❸ 将煎好之圆白菜饼盛于盘内，撒上青海苔、咸鱼末，淋些许陈醋即可食用。

【Methods】

❶ Mix (A) well.

❷ Warm 2 tbsp. oil in a pan, put (A) in and make it in round shape. Place 2 slices of meat on the cake, then fry the other side.

❸ Place the cooked cabbage cake on a plate, sprinkle (B) on it.

豆沙锅饼

Mashed Bean Pan-cake

【材料】

中筋面粉⋯⋯⋯⋯⋯⋯1 碗
甜豆沙⋯⋯⋯⋯⋯⋯250 克

【Ingredients】

1 bowl medium flour, 250g. sweet mashed bean

【作法】

❶ 面粉加水调成糊状。

❷ 热锅后加少许油，倒入面糊，于锅中滚匀成薄片，将豆沙抹在上面，面皮摺成方块状，两面稍煎，即可起锅。

❸ 另热5杯油，将煎好之豆沙饼放入锅中，炸成金黄色即可捞出切片食用。

【Methods】

❶ Mix flour with water to make paste.

❷ Heat the pan, add some oil, pour in the paste. Shake the pan back and forth to make a thin cake, spread the mashed bean on the cake, fold it, then fry both side.

❸ Heat 5 cups of oil, put the fried cake in, fry it till golden, slice and serve.

鲔鱼生菜沙拉

【材料】

油渍鲔鱼罐头…………一罐

(A)料：紫甘蓝丝、胡萝卜丝、
小黄瓜片、生菜剥口片
状、葡萄干、玉米粒。

(B)料：千岛沙拉酱、花生粉
（材料可依个人喜好酌量
增减）。

【作法】

❶ 将(A)料全部清洗，沥干水
分，置于大盘上。

❷ 去除鲔鱼罐头油质、鱼肉
置于(A)料之上。

❸ 冰凉后，将(B)料花生粉撒
在上面，并挤些沙拉酱，
风味更佳。

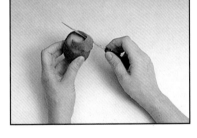

• •

Tuna Salad

【Ingredients】

Canned tuna

(A)sliced cabbage, carrot,
cucumber, lettuce, raisins,
corn bead

(B)thousand islands dressing,
peanut powder

【Methods】

❶Clean (A), drip dry.

❷Remove the oil of tuna, then
put tuna on (A).

❸Put them in refrigerator to
be cool, after that, sprinkle
peanut powder and pour
dressing over them.

清凉
水果甜汤

【材料】

什锦水果罐头…………一罐
杏仁豆腐………………一块
糖水 … … … … … … 适 量

【作法】

❶ 糖水可自己以砂糖加清水
调煮，或以市售果糖代
替。
❷ 杏仁豆腐切丁，倒入什锦
水果及所需的水量，加糖
水，置于冰箱中。冰后食
用倍觉清凉。

Sweet Fruit Soup

【Ingredients】

1 can of assorted fruit, almond jelly, sugar water

【Methods】

❶ Boil sugar and water.
❷ Cut almond jelly into cubes, add assorted fruit, water, and pour sugar water in, then put them in a refrigerator to be cold.

银耳
莲枣甜汤

【材料】

白木耳………………100 克
莲子…………………200 克
红枣、桂圆肉…………适量
砂糖…………………1 ½ 杯

【作法】

❶ 白木耳以清水泡软，莲子
洗净泡水 1 小时
❷ 莲子、红枣加水 8 杯，以
中火煮约 30 分钟，再放白
木耳、桂圆肉及糖续煮至
软即可。

Sweet Soup

【Ingredients】

100g. white fungus, 200g. lotus seeds, red date, longan pulp, 1½ cup of sugar

【Methods】

❶ Soak white fungus in water to be soft, clean lotus seeds and soak for 1 hour.
❷ Mix lotus seeds, red dates and 8 cups of water, cook in medium heat for 30 min. Then add white fungus, longan pulp and sugar to cook till they get soft.

123

碧兰鱿鱼

【材料】

素鱿鱼 ···2 块
口蘑 ··150 克
青花椰菜 ··¼棵
玉米笋 ···3 根
胡萝卜 ···¼ 条
红辣椒 ···2 根
姜 ···2 片

【调味料】

低钠盐 2 小匙、酱油 3 大匙、糖 1 大匙、陈醋 3 大匙。淀粉 2 大匙、香油少许。

【作法】

❶ 口蘑切半，胡萝卜切片，青花椰菜分小朵用盐水烫熟泡凉，玉米笋斜切成半后汆烫，红辣椒切丝。

❷ 起油锅，放入姜片、红辣椒丝爆香，再放入素鱿鱼略炒后依序加入口蘑及青花椰菜、玉米笋、胡萝卜拌炒，加入调味料 ❶，勾薄芡，起锅前淋上香油即可。

Vegetarian Squid with Green Vegetables

【Ingredients】

2 pieces of vegetarian squid, 150g. mushrooms, ¼ cauliflower, 3 corncobs, ¼ carrot, 2 chilli, 2 pieces of ginger

【Seasoning】

2 tbsp. of low sodiom salt, 3 tbsp. of soy sauce, 1 tbsp. of sugar, 3 tbsp. of black vinegar, 2 tbsp. of cornstarch, white sesame oil.

【Methods】

❶Cut mushroom to half, slice carrot, cut cauliflower by pieces and blanch by salty water, slice the corncobs and blanch, shredd chilli.

❷Heat oil, sante the ginger sliced, chilli shredded, add vegetarian squid, then mushrooms, cauliflower, corncobs carrot to fry, add ❶ spicies, thicken lightly, spread white sesame oil before turning off.

生菜虾松

【材料】

素虾仁……………………………………10 只
香菇………………………………………3 朵
胡萝卜……………………………………¼ 根
玉米笋……………………………………3 根
荸荠………………………………………4 个
生菜………………………………………10 片
老油条……………………………………1 条

【调味料】

低钠盐 2 小匙、酱油 1 大匙、糖 1 小匙、胡椒粉少许。

【作法】

❶ 素虾仁、香菇、胡萝卜、玉米笋、荸荠均切碎丁，老油条压碎，生菜洗净沥干水分备用。

❷ 素虾仁、香菇、胡萝卜、玉米笋、荸荠下锅略拌炒，再加调味料炒熟盛盘，加上碎油条拌匀。

❸ 以生菜叶包 ❷ 料即可食用。

Minced Shrimp with Lettuces

【Ingredients】

10 vegetarian shrimps, 3 black mushrooms,¼ carrot, 3 corncobs, 4 water chestnuts, 10 pieces of lettuces, 1 string of fried twisted dough

【Seasoning】

2 tbsp. of low sodium salt, 1 tbsp. of soy sauce, 1 tbsp. of sugar, pepper.

【Methods】

❶ Dice the shrimps, black mushrooms, carrot, corn, water chestnuts. Chop the fried twisted dough. Clean and drain lettuces.

❷ Fry the vegetarian shrimps,black mushrooms,carrot, corncobs and water chestnuts, add spicies, stir with fried twisted dough chopped.

❸ Wrape the ❷ ingredients by lettuce.

红烧栗子鸡

Simmer Chestnut Chicken

【材料】

素鸡················250 克
栗 子 ···············1 罐

【调味料】

糖2小匙、酱油3大匙、水3碗、淀粉1大匙、香油2大匙。

【作法】

❶ 素鸡撕成适口大小，入热油锅中炸呈金黄后捞起。

❷ 另起油锅，倒入素鸡、栗子略炒后加水、糖、酱油，以小火焖煮。

❸ 待❷锅中汤汁快干时，以水淀粉勾芡，盛盘后淋上香油即可。

【Ingredients】

250g. vegetarian chicken, 1 jar of chestnut

【Seasoning】

2 tbsp. of sugar, 3 tbsp. of soy sauce, 3 bowl of water, 1 tbsp. of cornstarch. 2 tbsp. of white sesame oil.

【Methods】

❶ Tear the vegetarian chicken to proper size, fry it till golden.

❷ Heat oil, fry the vegetarian chicken, chestnut, add water, sugar, soy sauce, stew by small fire.

❸ Until the soup going dry, thicken by cornstarch, spread white sesame oil before serving.

炒箭笋

Fry Smallcobs

【材料】

箭笋················500 克
香 菜 ···············少许

【调味料】

低钠盐1小匙、酱油1大匙、糖½小匙、香油1小匙、淀粉1大匙。

【作法】

❶ 箭笋洗净以沸水烫煮，再捞出冲冷水。

❷ 起油锅，放入箭笋加盐、酱油、糖拌炒后加水。续以小火焖煮至入味。

❸ 起锅前以水淀粉勾芡，盛盘后撒些香菜淋上香油即可。

【Ingredients】

500g. smallcobs, parsley

【Seasoning】

1 tbsp. of low sodium salt, 1 tbsp. of soy sauce, ½ tbsp. of sugar, 1 tbsp. of white sesame oil, 1 tbsp. of cornstarch.

【Methods】

❶ Clean the smallcobs and cook in boiling water, then keep in ice water.

❷ Heat oil, fry the smallcobs, add salt, soy sauce, sugar and water, stew by small fire.

❸ Thicken by cornstarch, spread on parsley and white sesame oil before serving.

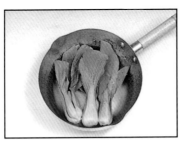

香菇菜心

【材料】

香菇 …………………………………………… 8 朵
油菜 …………………………………………… 1 把

【调味料】

低钠盐 2 小匙、素蚝油 2 大匙、糖 ½ 小匙、淀粉 1 大匙、香油少许。

【作法】

❶ 香菇洗净泡水后切半，油菜取中间部分洗净备用。

❷ 水煮沸后加入 2 小匙盐、1 大匙色拉油氽烫油菜后，置于冰水中半分钟，捞出沥干水分。

❸ 另起油锅，倒入香菇炒香，加入素蚝油、糖、盐后改小火煮至入味，勾薄芡后淋上香油后装盘，旁边铺围油菜即可。

Black Mushroom and Pickled Rapes

【Ingredients】

8 black mushrooms, 1 banch of rapes

【Seasoning】

2 tbsp. of low sodium salt, 2 tbsp. of vegetarian oyster sauce, ½ tbsp. of sugar, 1 tbsp. of cornstarch, white sesame oil.

【Methods】

❶Keep the mushrooms in water and cut to half, take the mid-part of rapes and clean them.

❷Add 2 tbsp. of salt and 1 tbsp. oil in boiling water, blanch the rapes, then cool them down for 30 secondes, drain.

❸Heat oil, sante the mushrooms, add vegetarian oyster sauce, sugar, salt to fry by small fire, thicken lightly and spread white sesame oil. Garnish by rapes on the sides.

131

什锦藕片

【材料】

莲藕	1 根
鲜香菇	4 朵
胡萝卜	半 根
豌豆荚	100 克
魔芋	50 克
姜	2 片

【调味料】

(A)料：酒、蚝油1大匙、酱油1小匙、盐1小匙、醋、糖少许。

(B)料：香油1小匙、淀粉少许。

【作法】

❶ 莲藕去皮切薄片，泡入醋水中防变黑。莲藕氽烫后捞出。

❷ 香菇斜切成3片，胡萝卜切长片与豌豆荚、魔芋入沸水中略烫。

❸ 香菇、姜爆香后将莲藕、胡萝卜、魔芋入锅拌炒，加入水少许、(A)料焖煮至入味，勾薄芡。

❹ 起锅前淋上香油即可。

Lotus Roots Assorted Vegetables

【Ingredients】

1 lotus roots, 4 black mushrooms, ½ carrot, 100g. bean peas, 50g. water arum, 2 pieces of gingers

【Seasoning】

(A)1 tbsp. of vegetarian oyster sauce, wine, 1 tbsp. of soy sauce. 1 tbsp. of salt, vinegar, sugar.

(B)1 tbsp. of white sesame oil, cornstarch.

【Methods】

❶Strip and slice the lotus roots, keep in vinegar water to avoid becoming black, blanch the lotus roots.

❷Trisect the black mushrooms, slice the carrot, blanch the ingredients with bean peas water arum in boiling water.

❸Sante black mushrooms, add lotus roots, carrot, water arum to fry, add a little of water, (A) spicies to stew, thicken.

❹spread white sesame oil before turning off.

红烧烤麸

【材料】

烤麸……………………8 个
胡萝卜…………………半根
竹笋……………………1 支
五香豆干………………3 块
姜………………………1 小块

【调味料】

(A)料：低钠盐 2 小匙、酱油 2 大匙、酒 1 大匙、糖 1 小匙。

(B)料：香油少许。

【作法】

❶ 烤麸剥成适口大小、入热油锅炸成金黄色，捞起沥油后备用。

❷ 竹笋、胡萝卜去皮切块，姜切片、豆干切三角片。

❸ 起油锅放入姜片爆香后，加笋块、豆干、胡萝卜、烤麸拌炒，加(A)料煮开，改小火焖煮至汤汁收干。

❹ 起锅前淋些香油即可。

Simmer Baked Bran

【Ingredients】

8 baked brans, ½ carrot, 1 bamboo shoot, 1 cube of ginger, 3 pieces of five spicies dry bean curd

【Seasoning】

(A) 2 tbsp. of low sodium salt, 2 tbsp. of soy sauce, 1 tbsp. of wine, 1 tbsp. of sugar.

(B) white sesame oil.

【Methods】

❶ Make the baked brans to the proper size, fried to golden, drain.

❷ Strip off and cube bamboo shoot and carrot, slice ginger and dry bean curd (like triangle).

❸ Heat oil, sante the ginger sliced, addcobs cube, dry bean curd, carrot, baked brans to fry, put (A) into, stir by small fire until the soup go to dry.

❹ Spread white sesame oil before turn off.

红烧苦瓜

【材料】

苦瓜……………………1 条
香菜…………………… 少许
鲜香菇…………………6 朵

【调味料】

酱油 6 大匙、冰糖 2 大匙、米酒 1 大匙、香油 1 大匙。

【作法】

❶ 苦瓜及鲜香菇洗净切块。

❷ 热油锅，将苦瓜、鲜香菇倒入炸约 3 分钟，捞出沥油。

❸ 另起油锅，倒入冰糖融化，再将苦瓜及鲜香菇重新入锅，加入酱油、米酒、水，改小火焖煮约 10 分钟，待汤汁收干后淋些香油，撒上香菜即可。

Simmer Bitter Gourd

【Ingredients】

1 bitter gourd, 6 mushrooms, parsley

【Seasoning】

6 tbsp. of soy sauce, 2 tbsp. of crystal sugar, 1 tbsp. of rice wine, 1 tbsp. of white sesame oil.

【Methods】

❶ Clean and cube the bitter gourd and mushroom.

❷ Heat oil, fried bitter gourd and mushroom for 3 minutes, strain them.

❸ Heat another oil, put the crystal sugar on, add the bitter gourd and mushroom, soy sauce, rice wine, water, stew for 10 minutes. Until the soup going dry, spread white sesame oil and parsley.

135

豆苗虾仁

【材料】

豆苗 ···································· 250 克
素虾仁 ·································· 1 杯
姜 ······································ 2 片

【调味料】

低钠盐2小匙、素蚝油1大匙、糖1小匙、香油1小匙、淀粉少许、胡椒少许。

【作法】

❶ 豆苗洗净后放入沸水中加少许盐、色拉油氽烫后捞出冲冷水，装盘。

❷ 起油锅，倒入姜末爆香后加入素虾仁拌炒加1小匙盐、蚝油、糖、胡椒粉调味，以水淀粉勾薄芡后淋上香油，起锅铺在豆苗上即可。

Fry Bean Sprouts with Vegetarian Shrimp

【Ingredients】

250g. bean sprouts, 1 cup of vegetarian shrimps, 2 pieces of ginger

【Seasoning】

2 tbsp. of low sodium salt, 1 tbsp. of vegetarian oyster sauce, 1 tbsp. of sugar, 1 tbsp. of white sesame oil, cornstarch, pepper.

【Methods】

❶Clean and blanch the bean sprouts in boiling water after adding a dash of salt, oil, then cool down, put them on dish.

❷Heat oil, sante ginger shredded, add vegetarian shrimps, 1 tbsp. of salt, vegetarian oyster sauce, sugar, pepper. thicken by cornstarch and spread white sesame oil. Put them on the bean sprouts of the dish.

咕咾肉

【材料】

烤麸···5 个
面粉···1 碗
菠萝···1 片
青椒、红椒·································各 1 个
姜···1 片

【调味料】

低钠盐 2 小匙、糖 1 大匙、番茄酱 2 大匙、醋 1 小匙、淀粉 1 大匙。

【作法】

❶ 烤麸洗净挤干水分，撕适口大小，菠萝、青椒、红椒切小片状，姜片切末。

❷ 面粉加水调成面糊。烤麸沾裹面糊后，入热油锅中炸呈金黄色，捞出备用。

❸ 另起油锅炒香姜末，再倒入菠萝、青、红椒快炒，加上盐、糖、番茄酱、醋、水淀粉调味勾芡后，再将炸酥的烤麸入锅拌匀即可。

Gu-Lao Meat

【Ingredients】

5 baked bran, 1 bowl of flour, 1 piece of pineapple, 1 green and 1 red bell pepper, 1 piece of gingar

【Seasoning】

2 tbsp. of low sodium salt, 1 tbsp of sugar, 2 tbsp. of ketchup, 1 tbsp. of vinegar, 1 tbsp. of cornstarch.

【Methods】

❶ Clean and dry the baked bran, tear it. Slice the pineapple, green and red bell pepper, shred the ginger.

❷ Flour and water mix to batter, put the batter on the baked bran, fried to golden.

❸ Heat oil, sante the shredded ginger, add pineapple, green and red bell pepper, then put the salt, sugar, ketchup, vinegar on, thicken by cornstarch, stir with baked bran.

凉拌长生果

【材料】

花生仁……………250 克
小黄瓜……………2 条
胡萝卜……………1/3 根

【调味料】

低钠盐5小匙、糖1小匙、香油2小匙。

【作法】

❶ 花生仁洗净泡水1小时。水锅中煮溶3小匙盐后，放入花生仁以小火焖煮1小时，待熟软即可盛盘。

❷ 小黄瓜去头尾洗净切丁。胡萝卜削皮洗净切丁，以沸水煮熟。

❸ 小黄瓜丁、胡萝卜丁拌入花生内，再加2小匙盐、1小匙糖和2小匙香油搅匀即可。

Cold Dressed Peanut

【Ingredients】

250g. Peanuts, 2 cucumbers, 1/3 carrot

【Seasoning】

5 tbsp. of low sodium salt, 1 tbsp. of sugar, 2 tbsp. of white sesame oil.

【Methods】

❶ Clean the peanut and keep in the water for 1 hour. Add 3 tbsp. of salt in heated water, stew peanuts for 1 hour until become soft and well - done, put them on the dish.

❷ Clean and dice the cucumbers and carrot, cook by boiling water.

❸ Mix cucumbers and carrot with peanuts, stir with 2 tbsp. of salt, 1tbsp. of sugar, 2 tbsp. of white sesame oil.

凉拌豆腐

【材料】

嫩豆腐……………2 盒
小黄瓜……………1 条
胡萝卜……………1/3 根
香菜…………… 少许

【调味料】

低钠盐2小匙、酱油2大匙、糖1大匙、醋1大匙、香油少许。

【作法】

❶ 豆腐以开水氽烫后盛盘。

❷ 小黄瓜去头尾洗净刨丝，胡萝卜削皮洗净刨丝，饰于盘边。

❸ 将调味料调匀，淋于豆腐上食用。

Cold Dressed Dou-Fu

【Ingredients】

2 boxes of Dou-Fu, 1 cucumber, 1/3 carrot, a dash of parsley

【Seasoning】

2 tbsp. of low sodium salt, 2 tbsp. of soy sauce, 1 tbsp. of sugar, 1 tbsp. of vinegar, a dash of white sesame oil.

【Methods】

❶ Blanch the Dou-Fu, put them on the dish.

❷ Clean and shred the cucumber and carrot, garnish on the edge of the dish.

❸ Mixing the spicies, dressing on the top of Dou-Fu.

糖醋鱼片

【材料】

素鱼……………………………………………1 条
菠萝……………………………………………2 片
青椒、红椒…………………………………各 1 条
香菜……………………………………………少许

【调味料】

低钠盐 2 小匙、糖 ½ 大匙、醋 1 小匙、番茄酱 2 大匙、水淀粉 1 大匙、香油 1 小匙。

【作法】

❶ 菠萝切丁，青椒、红椒去籽切斜片。
❷ 热油炸素鱼，待呈金黄色后捞起切斜块盛盘。
❸ 另起油锅，将菠萝、青椒、红椒加少许水略炒。
❹ 加盐、糖、醋、番茄酱入 ❸ 锅中同炒，入味后以水淀粉勾芡，起锅前加香油淋于素鱼上，并以香菜点缀即可。

Sweet Vinegar Fish Fillet

【Ingredients】

1 vegetarian Fish, 2 pieces of pineapple, 1 green bell pepper, 1 red bell pepper, parsley

【Seasoning】

2 tbsp. of low sodium salt, ½ tbsp. of sugar, 1 tbsp. of vinegar, 2 tbsp. of ketchup, 1 tbsp. of cornstarch water, 1 tbsp. of white sesame oil.

【Methods】

❶Cube the pineapple, keep the seeds of green bell pepper and red bell pepper away, sliced.
❷Fry the fish until golden, cube and put them on.
❸Heat oil, fry the pineapple, green and red bell pepper with a little of water.
❹Going on to add salt, sugar, vinegar, ketchup, thicken by starch water, spread white sesame oil on the fish before closing fire. Garnish by parsley.

143

粉蒸肉

【材料】

粉肠 ……………………………………… 2 条
地瓜 ……………………………………… 1 大个
蒸肉粉 …………………………………… 2 包
香菜 ……………………………………… 少许

【调味料】

低钠盐 1 小匙、酱油 1 大匙、糖 1 大匙、米酒 1 大匙、姜末 ½ 大匙、香油 1 小匙、甜面酱 1 大匙、胡椒少许。

【作法】

❶ 粉肠撕适口大小，地瓜去皮切块。

❷ 调味料调匀，与粉肠一同倒入大碗中搅拌后腌 20 分钟。

❸ 蒸肉粉倒进另一只大碗中，从调味料中挑出粉肠入内拌匀，加 1 大匙水及香油放入蒸碗里，先排上粉肠再排地瓜，在蒸锅里以中火蒸半小时，起锅后倒扣入盘，撒些香菜即可。

Steam Meat

【Ingredients】

2 strips of flour dough, 1 sweet potato, 2 pack of steam flour, parsley

【Seasoning】

1 tbsp. of low sodium salt, 1 tbsp. of soy sauce, 1 tbsp. of sugar, 1 tbsp. of rice wine, ½ tbsp. of shredded ginger, 1 tbsp. of white sesame oil, 1 tbsp. of sweet - flour sauce, pepper.

【Methods】

❶Tear the flour dough to proper size, strip and cube the sweet potato.

❷Mix the spicies, stir with flour dough, put in the large bowl, keep it for 20 minutes.

❸Put the Steam flour to another bowl, stir with flour dough from spicies, add 1 tbsp. of water and white sesame oil to the steam bowl, put the flour dough then sweet potato on. Steam for 1 hour. Spread parsley before serving.

香芹豆干

【材料】

芹菜‥‥‥‥‥‥‥‥‥‥2 棵
五香豆干‥‥‥‥‥‥‥‥8 片
红辣椒‥‥‥‥‥‥‥‥‥1 条
胡萝卜‥‥‥‥‥‥‥‥1 小块

【调味料】

低钠盐 2 小匙、酱油 1 大匙、
糖 1 大匙。

【作法】

❶ 芹菜切段，豆干切片，胡
萝卜切细丝，红椒切末。
❷ 起油锅，放入豆干炒香盛
起备用。
❸ 另起油锅，加入芹菜、红
辣椒、胡萝卜丝，加少许
水略炒，加调味料拌炒即
可。

Celery and Dry Bean Curd

【Ingredients】

2 celery, 8 pieces of five spicies dry bean curd, 1 chilli, 1 cube of carrot

【Seasoning】

2 tbsp. of low sodium salt, 1 tbsp. soy sauce, 1 tbsp. of sugar.

【Methods】

❶ Cut the celery by pieces, slice the dry bean curd, shred the carrot, chop the chilli.
❷ Heat oil, fry the dry bean curd.
❸ Heat another oil, fry the celery, chilli, carrot shredded, and a little of water, add the spicies.

宫保甜椒

【材料】

素肉‥‥‥‥‥‥‥ 100 克
青椒‥‥‥‥‥‥‥½ 个
红椒‥‥‥‥‥‥‥1 个
黄椒‥‥‥‥‥‥‥1 个

【调味料】

调味酱 2 大匙、水少许。

【作法】

❶ 青椒、红椒、黄椒均去籽
切块。
❷ 起油锅，放入素肉、青椒、
红椒、黄椒炒熟。
❸ 调味酱加些水化开，倒入
❷ 的锅中拌炒入味即可。

Spicy Sweet Bell Pepper

【Ingredients】

100g. vegetarian meat,½ green bell pepper, 1 red bell pepper, 1 yellow bell pepper

【Seasoning】

2 tbsp. of spicy sauce, water.

【Methods】

❶ Cube the green, red, yellow bell pepper.
❷ Heat oil, fry the vegetarian meat, green, red, yellow bell pepper.
❸ Add water into the spicy sauce, pour into ❷, stir.

红烧肉

【材料】

水面筋 ·· 3 个
竹笋 ·· 1 支
香菇 ·· 4 朵
胡萝卜 ·· ½ 个

【调味料】

低钠盐 1 小匙、糖 1 大匙、酱油 4 大匙、水适量、香油 1 小匙、酒少许。

【作法】

❶ 水面筋撕成块状，入冷油锅加热，以中火炸酥，竹笋剥皮洗净切块。香菇泡软切成 4 小块、胡萝卜切小块。

❷ 炸好的水面筋另加 4 碗冷水以大火煮软，捞出，沥干水分。

❸ 起油锅炒竹笋、香菇、胡萝卜，加入调味料及水面筋以中火煮开，再以小火焖煮至汤汁收干，起锅前撒上香油即可。

Simmer Meat

【Ingredients】

3 round flour dough, 1 bamboo shoot. 4 mushrooms, ½ carrot

【Seasoning】

1 tbsp. of low sodium salt, 1 tbsp. of sugar, 4 tbsp. of soy sance, water, 1 tbsp. of white sesame oil, wine.

【Methods】

❶ Tear the flour dough to cube, fried by midfire, strip and cube the bamboo shoot. keep Mushroom in water to be soft and cut into 4 pieces, cube carrot.

❷ Add 4 bowls of water to the flour dough and stew by large fire, then strain them.

❸ Heat oil, frycobs, mushroom, carrot, add spicies and flour dough, stew by midfire, then by small - fire until the soup going dry. Spread white sesame oil before turning off.

白果虾仁

【材料】
素虾仁 …………………………………………… 1 碗
白果 ……………………………………………… 1 罐
素火腿 ………………………………………… 1 小块
小黄瓜 …………………………………………… 1 条

【调味料】
低钠盐 2 小匙、糖 1 小匙、米酒 1 小匙、香油 1 小匙。

【作法】
❶ 以沸水汆烫素虾仁、白果，沥干。素火腿、小黄瓜切丁。
❷ 起油锅放入素火腿、小黄瓜快炒，再放入虾仁、白果、调味料拌炒，起锅前淋上香油即可。

Fry Nut with Shrimp

【Ingredients】
1 bowl of vegetarian shrimp, 1 jar of nuts, 1 cube of vegetarian ham, 1 cucumber

【Seasoning】
2 tbsp. of low sodium salt, 1 tbsp. of sugar, 1 tbsp of rice wine, 1 tbsp. of white sesame oil.

【Methods】
❶Blanch the vegetarian shrimp, nuts and strain. Cube the vegetarian ham and cucumber.
❷Heat oil, fry the vegetarian ham, cucumber, add shrimps, nuts, spicies, spread white sesame oil before closing fire.

151

雪菜豆皮

【材料】

雪菜…………………150 克
豆皮………………… 6 张
红辣椒………………¼ 个
碱………………………½ 块

【调味料】

低钠盐2小匙、米酒1大匙、香油2大匙。

【作法】

❶ 雪菜去尾洗净切末，豆皮切末，以温碱水泡至变白，再以冷水洗净，红椒切细丁。

❷ 起油锅，先将雪菜、红椒炒香后，放入豆皮同炒，加盐、酒调味拌炒后加水煮约5分钟，改大火收干汤汁，淋上香油即可。

Pickled Mustard Green with Dou-Pi

【Ingredients】

150g. pickled mustard green, 6 piece of Dou-Pi, ¼ chilli, ½ piece of alkali

【Seasoning】

2 tbsp. of low sodium salt, 1 tbsp. of rice wine, 2 tbsp. of white sesame oil.

【Methods】

❶ Clean and chop the pickled mustard green, chop the Dou-Pi, keep it in alkali water to be white, clean by cold water, dice the chilli.

❷ Heat oil, fry the pickled mustard green, chilli, add Dou-Pi, stew with salt, wine, water for 5 minutes, turn to large fire until dry, spread white sesame oil.

香芝面肠

【材料】

面肠………………… 3 条

【调味料】

酱油4大匙、糖1小匙、香油1小匙、白芝麻1大匙、姜1片。

【作法】

❶ 面肠切片，姜切末。
❷ 白芝麻干炒备用。
❸ 热油，以中火炸面肠，待呈金黄色，即捞出沥干油分。锅内留少许油，加入调味料与炸过的面肠迅速拌抄盛盘，再撒上白芝麻即可。

Vegetarian Sesame Sausage

【Ingredients】

3 strings of flour sausage

【Seasoning】

4 tbsp. of soy sauce, 1 tbsp. of sugar, 1 tbsp. of white sesame oil, 1 tbsp. of white sesame, 1 piece of ginger.

【Methods】

❶ Slice the flour sausage, chop the ginger.
❷ Dry-fry the white sesame.
❸ Heat oil, fry the flour sausage by mid-fire till golden, drain. Keep a little bit oil inside, add spicies and fried flour sausage to fry guickly, remove, spread white sesames.

酱爆猴菇

【材料】
猴头菇 ………………………………………………… 1 罐
青椒 …………………………………………………… 1 个
红椒 …………………………………………………… 1 个
黄椒 …………………………………………………… 1 个

【调味料】
(A)料：酱油、辣豆瓣酱各 1 大匙。
(B)料：香油少许。

【作法】
❶ 猴头菇余烫后剥成适口大小。
❷ 青椒、红椒、黄椒去籽，切片。
❸ 热油炸猴头菇，呈金黄色捞起沥油备用。
❹ 另起油锅，倒入青椒、红椒、黄椒略炒，再加猴头菇同炒，最后加(A)料拌匀，起锅前淋上香油即可。

Sante Monkey-Head Mushrooms

【Ingredients】
1 jar of monkey-head mushrooms, 1 green bell pepper, 1 red bell pepper, 1 yellow bell pepper

【Seasoning】
(A)1 tbsp. of soy sauce and 1 tbsp. spicy bean sauce.
(B)white sesame oil.

【Methods】
❶Blanch the monkey-head mushrooms and tear to proper size.
❷Keep the seeds of green bell pepper, red bell pepper, yellow bell pepper away, and slice.
❸Fry the monkey-head mushrooms to golden, drain.
❹Heat another oil, fry the green, red, yellow bell pepper, add monkey-head mushrooms, stir with (A) spicies, spread white sesame oil before turning off.

红烧豆腐

【材料】

豆腐 …………………………………………… 1 块
竹笋 …………………………………………… 1 支
香菇 …………………………………………… 3 朵
青椒 …………………………………………… ½ 个
红辣椒 ………………………………………… 1 根
姜 ……………………………………………… 2 片
香油…………………………………………… 1 小匙

【调味料】

低钠盐 1 小匙、酱油 3 大匙、糖 1 大匙、淀粉 2 大匙、胡椒粉少许。

【作法】

❶ 豆腐横切成三角形，竹笋去皮切片，香菇泡软去蒂切长条，青椒去籽切块，红辣椒切丝。

❷ 热油锅，放入豆腐炸成金黄色后捞出。

❸ 另起油锅，先爆香姜片、红辣椒，再倒入笋片、香菇、青椒拌炒，最后放入豆腐，淋调味汁调味勾芡，再淋上香油即可。

Simmer Dou-Fu

【Ingredients】

1 cube of Dou-Fu (long - shape), 3 black mushrooms, 1 bamboo shoot, ½ green bell pepper, 1 chilli, 2 pieces of ginger, 1 tbsp. of white sesame oil

【Seasoning】

1 tbsp. of low sodium salt, 3 tbsp. of soy sauce, 1 tbsp. of sugar, 2 tbsp. of cornstarch, pepper.

【Methods】

❶Cut the Dou-Fu to triangle, strip and slice bamboo shoot, soften the black mushroom, cut the stems off, and shred, cube the green bell pepper, shredd chilli.

❷Heat oil, fry Dou-Fu till golden.

❸Heat another oil, sante ginger, chilli, add bamboo shoots slices, black mushrooms, green bell pepper to fry and Dou-Fu, sprinkle spicies and thicken, spread white sesame oil.

酥炸香菇

【材料】
鲜香菇‥‥‥‥‥‥‥‥10 朵
煎炸粉‥‥‥‥‥‥‥‥1 杯
【调味料】
胡椒盐适量。

【作法】
❶ 鲜香菇洗净去蒂，并在菇
　伞上划十字。
❷ 煎炸粉加水调匀成面糊。
❸ 香菇一一沾②的面糊下
　锅油炸，待呈金黄色即可
　捞出盛盘，食用时沾胡椒
　盐。

Fry Mushroom

【Ingredients】
10 mushrooms, 1 cup of fry flour
【Seasoning】
pepper.
【Mehtods】
❶Clean and keep the mushroom stem away, cut cross on the cap.
❷Mix fry flour and water to batter.
❸Put the batter on the mushroom and fry them until golden. Serve with pepper.

• •

炸明虾

【材料】
素明虾‥‥‥‥‥‥‥‥8 只
蛋‥‥‥‥‥‥‥‥‥‥1 个
煎炸粉‥‥‥‥‥‥‥‥1 碗
水‥‥‥‥‥‥‥‥‥‥1 碗
【调味料】
甜辣酱适量。

【作法】
❶ 在大碗中打蛋，加水及煎
　炸粉搅匀。
❷ 以素明虾沾❶的面糊，入
　热油锅炸至金黄色，捞出
　沥油。
❸ 可沾甜辣酱食用。

Fry King Prawn

【Ingredients】
8 king prawns, 1 egg, 1 bowl of fry flour, 1 bowl of water
【Seasoning】
sweet-spicy sauce.
【Methods】
❶Stir a egg in big bowl, then add water and fry flour.
❷Put the king prawn in ❶, fry until golden and strain it.
❸Serve with sweet-spicy sauce.

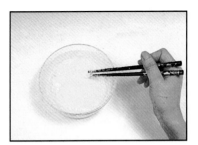

罗汉斋

【材料】

白果	12 颗
素虾仁	150 克
胡萝卜	1 根
白萝卜	1 根
草菇	6 朵
鲜香菇	3 朵
玉米笋	3 根
青花椰菜	1 棵

【调味料】

(A)料：低钠盐2小匙、酱油2大匙、糖1小匙、水1碗、胡椒少许。

(B)料：淀粉、香油各1大匙。

【作法】

❶ 青花椰菜氽烫30秒捞出，盐1小匙、香油1大匙调匀拌入青花椰菜内，铺于盘沿备用。

❷ 白果、草菇烫熟，胡萝卜、白萝卜挖成圆球状，鲜香菇切丁，玉米笋切粗丁。

❸ 先爆香香菇、素虾仁，再放入胡萝卜、白萝卜、草菇、玉米笋炒熟。

❹ (A)料调匀后入 ❸ 拌炒，以水淀粉勾芡，淋上香油即可。

Vegetarian Meal for Buddhism

【Ingredients】

12 nuts, 150g. vegetarian shrimp, 1 carrot, 1 radish, 6 mushrooms, 3 black mushrooms, 3 corncobs, 1 cauliflower

【Seasoning】

(A)2 tbsp. of low sodium salt, 2 tbsp. of soy sauce, 1 tbsp. of sugar, 1 bowl of water, pepper.

(B)1 tbsp. of cornstarch and 1 tbsp. of white sesame oil.

【Methods】

❶Blanch cauliflower for 30 seconds, stir with 1 tbsp. of salt, 1 tbsp. of white sesame oil, put on the edge of the dish.

❷Cook the nuts, mushrooms, make the carrot, radish in to ball-shape. Dice black mushrooms, cube corncobs.

❸Sante black mushrooms, vegetarian shrimps, add carrot, radish, mushrooms, corncobs to fry.

❹Mix (A) spicies, add into ❸ to fry, thicken by cornstarch, spread white sesame oil.

什锦锅

【材料】

大白菜	半棵	竹笋	½ 支
豆腐	1 块	炸芋头	4 块
香菇	4 朵	青花椰菜	¼ 棵
金针菇	1 小把	红辣椒	1 根
玉米笋	3 根	胡萝卜	½ 根
素丸	5 个	姜	1 小块
木耳	2 片		

【调味料】

低钠盐少许、素高汤适量、酱油1小匙、素调味酱适量。

【作法】

❶ 大白菜洗净切大块，豆腐切片，香菇泡软去蒂，金针菇、青花椰菜氽烫分小朵，玉米笋直切成半，木耳切长条，竹笋、胡萝卜去皮切长片，姜切末。

❷ 将所有的材料入锅排放整齐，注入高汤，加上调味料煮熟。

❸ 可沾酱油加姜末或素调味酱食用。

Combination Soup

【Ingredients】

½ Chinese cabbage, 1 cube of Dou-Fu, 4 black mushrooms, 1 banch of golden mushrooms, 3 corncobs, 5 meatless balls, 2 edible fungus, ½ bamboo shoot, 4 fried taro, ¼ cauliflower, 1 chilli, ½ carrot, 1 cube of ginger

【Seasoning】

A dash of low sodium salt, vegetarian broth, 1 tbsp. of soy sauce, vegetarian barbecue sauce.

【Methods】

❶ Clean and cut the Chinese cabbage (large cube), slice Dou-Fu. Cut the stems of black mushrooms off. Blanch the golden mushrooms and cauliflower, cut into small size, and cut the corncobs straight, agaric by strings. Strip and slice the bamboo shoot and carrot. Chop ginger.

❷ Put all ingredients in the pan orderly, pour broth in, add spicies and cookwell.

❸ Serve with soy sauce and ginger or vegetarian barbecue sauce.

酥炸虾球

【材料】
马铃薯、蛋白⋯⋯⋯各1个
胡萝卜⋯⋯⋯⋯⋯⋯1根
荸荠⋯⋯⋯⋯⋯⋯⋯8个
芹菜⋯⋯⋯⋯⋯⋯⋯2根
淀粉⋯⋯⋯⋯⋯⋯3大匙
椒盐、甜辣酱⋯⋯⋯适量

【调味料】
低钠盐1小匙、胡椒少许、香油1小匙。

【作法】
❶ 马铃薯去皮切片，蒸15分钟取出切碎。胡萝卜、荸荠切碎，芹菜去叶切末。
❷ 马铃薯泥、胡萝卜、荸荠、芹菜加上调味料和淀粉、蛋白搅匀，待有弹性后再揉成圆球状。
❸ 热油锅炸虾球，至金黄色捞出。食用时可沾椒盐或甜辣酱。

Fry Shrimp Ball

【Ingredients】
1 potato, 1 carrot, 8 water chestnuts, 2 celery, 1 egg-white, 3 tbsp. of cornstarch, pepper-salt, sweet-spicy sauce

【Seasoning】
1 tbsp. of low sodium salt, 1 tbsp. of white sesame oil, pepper.

【Methods】
❶ Strip and slice the potato, steam for 15 minutes and chop it. Shred the carrot, water chestnuts and celery (No-Leaves).
❷ Stir with potato, carrot, waterchestnut, celery, spicies, cornstarch and egg-white. Then make it like a ball.
❸ Fry the balls until golden. Serving with pepper salt or sweet - spicy sauce.

香酥豆腐

【材料】
豆腐⋯⋯⋯⋯⋯⋯2大块
蛋⋯⋯⋯⋯⋯⋯⋯1个
煎炸粉⋯⋯⋯⋯⋯1碗

【调味料】
胡椒盐适量、甜辣酱适量。

【作法】
❶ 豆腐先切长条，再横切小块。
❷ 豆腐先沾蛋液，再沾裹煎炸粉。
❸ 热油，放入豆腐炸至金黄色捞出。食用时可沾胡椒盐或甜辣酱。

Deep-Fried Dou-Fu

【Ingredients】
2 pieces of Dou-Fu, 1 egg, 1 bowl of fry flour

【Seasoning】
Pepper, sweet-spicy sauce.

【Methods】
❶ Cut the Dou-Fu to strings, then cube.
❷ Put the egg-stired on the Dou-Fu, then fry-flour on.
❸ Heat oil, fried the Dou-Fu until golden. Serve with pepper or sweet-spicy sauce.

咖哩口蘑

【材料】
口蘑………………200 克
胡萝卜………………1 根
姜…………………1 小块
青豆仁………………少许
玉米笋………………3 根
香菜…………………少许

【调味料】
(A)料：低钠盐 2 小匙、咖哩
粉适量。
(B)料：淀粉 1 小匙、香油 1 小
匙。

【作法】
❶ 口蘑对切，胡萝卜、玉米
笋切丁。青豆仁先煮熟。
❷ 起油锅，先爆香姜片再倒
入口蘑、青豆仁、玉米笋
略炒后，加(A)料拌炒入味
后勾芡，淋上香油。
❸ 盛盘后以香菜点缀。

Curry Mushroom

【Ingredients】
200g. mushrooms, 1 cube of
carrot, 1 cube of ginger, green
peas, 3 corncobs, parsley
【Seasoning】
(A)2 tbsp. of low sodium salt,
curry powder.
(B)1 tbsp. of cornstarch, 1 tbsp.
of white sesame oil.
【Methods】
❶Cut the mushrooms across,
dice carrot, corncobs, cook
the green peas.
❷Heat oil, sante the sliced
ginger, add mushroom,
green peas, corncobs to fry,
put (A) in and thicken,
spread sesame oil.
❸Garnish by parsley before
serving.

金针菇芥菜

【材料】
金针菇………………1 大把
芥菜…………………2 小棵
姜末…………………少许

【调味料】
低钠盐 2 小匙、高汤 2 碗、香
油 1 小匙、淀粉 1 大匙。

【作法】
❶ 金针菇去尾尖烫捞出备
用。
❷ 芥菜去叶取中间部分，切
半烫软，泡凉。
❸ 起油锅，爆香姜末后，芥
菜入锅略炒，加盐、高汤
小火焖煮 5 分钟，盛盘。另
起油锅，倒入金针菇加少
许盐，1 小匙酱油拌炒后
勾芡，淋上香油即可。

Golden Mushroom with Mustard Plant

【Ingredients】
1 banch of golden mushrooms,
2 mustard plants, ginger
chopped
【Seasoning】
2 tbsp. of low sodium salt, 2
bowl of broth, 1 tbsp. of white
sesame oil, 1 tbsp. of cornstarch.
【Methods】
❶Cut the bottom of golden
mushrooms and blanch.
❷Mustard plants no leaves
and take the mid-parts, cut
to half and blanch soft,
keep in cold water.
❸ Heat oil, sante ginger
chopped, add mustard
plants to fry, stew with salt,
broth by small fire for 5
minutes, remove. Heat an-
other oil, fry the golden
mushroom add salt, 1 tbsp.
of soy sauce, thicken,
spread white sesame oil.

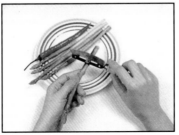

芦笋百合

【材料】

绿芦笋 ·· 5 根
新鲜百合 ······································ 100 克
鲜香菇 ·· 2 朵
红辣椒 ·· 1 个
黄椒 ··· 1 个

【调味料】

低钠盐 2 小匙、糖 ½ 小匙。

【作法】

❶ 芦笋去皮切小段，鲜百合洗净剥开切片，鲜香菇
去蒂切丝，红辣椒切丝，黄椒切块。

❷ 先爆香香菇、红辣椒，再将芦笋、百合、黄椒倒
入，以大火快炒，加盐、糖调味后即可盛盘。

Asparagus with Lily

【Ingredients】

5 green asparagus, 100g. fresh lily, 2 black mushrooms,
1 chilli, 1 yellow bell pepper

【Seasoning】

2 tbsp. of low sodium salt, ½ tbsp. of sugar.

【Methods】

❶Strip the asparagus and cut by pieces, strip and slice
the fresh lilies. Cut the stems of black mushrooms
and shred, shred chilli, dice yellow bell pepper.

❷Sante black mushroom, chilli, add asparagus, lilies,
yellow bell pepper to fry by large fire. Add salt,
sugar to season, then remove.

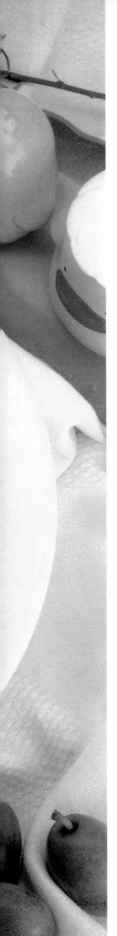

双菇烩虾仁

【材料】
鲜香菇…………………………………………5 朵
平菇………………………………………150 克
素虾仁………………………………………1 小 碗
青豆仁…………………………………………少许
胡萝卜…………………………………………少许
香菜……………………………………………少许

【调味料】
低钠盐2小匙、酱油2大匙、胡椒少许、淀粉、香油各1大匙。

【作法】
❶ 鲜香菇去蒂切粗丝，平菇汆烫备用。
❷ 鲜香菇、平菇爆香，再加素虾仁、青豆仁、胡萝卜丁炒熟后加盐、酱油和少许水以中火稍焖热后勾芡。
❸ 起锅前加少许胡椒粉，淋上香油，盛盘后撒些香菜即可。

Fry Mushroom with Shrimp

【Ingredients】
5 fresh mushrooms, 150g. mini mushroom, 1 small bowl of vegetarian shrimp, green peas, carrot, parsley

【Seasoning】
2 tbsp. of low sodium salt, 2 tbsp. of soy sauce, pepper, 1 tbsp. of cornstarch, 1 tbsp. of white sesame oil.

【Methods】
❶Keep the stems of fresh mushrooms away, and slice, blanch the mini mushroom.
❷Sante fresh mushroom and mini mushrooms, add shrimps, green peas, carrot cube until well - done, stir with salt, soy sauce and a little of water by mid - fire, then thicken.
❸Add a dash of pepper, white sesame oil before turn off, spread parsley on the dish.

珍珠丸子

【材料】

面肠⋯2 条　　芋头⋯¼ 个
香菇⋯3 朵　　豌豆仁⋯少许
荸荠⋯6 个　　淀粉 2 大匙
糯米⋯1 碗

【调味料】

低钠盐 1 小匙、酱油 2 大匙、糖 1 小匙、胡椒 ½ 小匙、地瓜粉 8 大匙。

【作法】

❶ 面肠切碎，芋头去皮切小丁、香菇、荸荠剁碎。

❷ 芋头丁加 1 小匙酱油拌匀后，以热油炸熟。

❸ 碎面肠加入芋头、香菇、荸荠及调味料等放入大碗中用手抓拌成内馅。

❹ 糯米泡过后沥干水分，加 2 大匙淀粉置于盘中。

❺ 将 ❸ 捏成球状后沾裹糯米，以大火蒸 15 分钟，起锅后以豌豆仁点缀。

Pearl Pill

【Ingredients】

2 flour dough, ¼ taro, 3 mushrooms, 6 water chestnut, 1 bowl of glutinous rice, splitpeas, 2 tbsp. of cornstarch.

【Seasoning】

1 tbsp. of low sodium salt, 2 tbsp. of soy sauce, 1 tbsp. of sugar, ½ tbsp. of pepper, 8 tbsp. of sweet potato flour

【Methods】

❶Chop the flour dough, strip and cube taro, shred the mushrooms and water chestnuts.

❷Taro cubes stir with 1 tbsp. soy sauce, fry till well-done.

❸Add taro, mushroom, water chestnut and spicies in flour dough, put them in a large bowl, and stir with hands.

❹Glutinous rice keep in water and strain it, add 2 tbsp. of cornstarch, put them on the dish.

❺ Make the dough ❸ like a ball, and put the glutinous rice on. Steam by large fire for 15 minutes. Garnish by splitpeas.

酥炸芋球

【材料】

大芋头 1 个、素火腿 1 小块、胡萝卜 1 小块、玉米粒 ½ 杯、芹菜 1 根、面粉适量、蛋 2 个、面包粉适量。

【调味料】

低钠盐少许、胡椒少许、香油少许、番茄酱适量。

【作法】

❶ 芋头切厚片蒸软，趁热捣烂并撒上盐、胡椒拌匀。素火腿、胡萝卜切细丁，芹菜切末，蛋打散。

❷ 起油锅，爆香素火腿、芹菜末，再倒入胡萝卜、玉米粒炒熟，盛起放凉。

❸ 将芋泥及少量面粉拌匀，分成 10 等分，再包入 ❷ 的馅料，沾裹煎炸粉入热油锅炸成金黄色，捞出沥油，可沾番茄酱食用。

Deep-Fried Taro Ball

【Ingredients】

1 big taro, 1 cube of vegetarian ham, 1 cube of carrot, ½ cup of corn, 1 celery, 2 eggs, flour and bread flour

【Seasoning】

low sodium salt, pepper, white sesame oil, ketchup.

【Methods】

❶ Slice the taro thick and steam till soft, chop the taro and add salt, pepper. Cube the vegetarian ham and carrot, chop the celery, stir the eggs.

❷Heat oil, sante the vegetarian ham and celery chopped, add carrot, corn.

❸Stir the taro chopped and a little flour, cut into 10 pieces, put the ingredients ❷ inside, put the fry-flour in and fry till golden, drain. Serve with ketchup.

173

九层鳝糊

【材料】

香菇 ……………………………………………… 8 朵
金针菇 ………………………………………… 1 大把
素火腿 ………………………………………… 1 小块
胡萝卜、竹笋 ……………………………… 各 1 小块
淀粉 …………………………………………… 1 小碗
紫苏 …………………………………………… 适量

【调味料】

(A)低钠盐 1 小匙、素蚝油、酱油各 1 大匙、糖 1 小匙。

(B)料：香油 1 小匙、淀粉 1 大匙。

【作法】

❶ 金针菇氽烫捞出备用。素火腿、胡萝卜、竹笋切丝。

❷ 香菇泡软去蒂，顺着菇缘剪成长条状，外沾淀粉入锅油炸。

❸ 起油锅时，将素火腿、素鳝鱼、竹笋、胡萝卜、金针菇同炒，加(A)料后勾芡。

❹ 起锅前加入紫苏，淋上香油即可。

Fry Vegetarian Eel-paste and Basil

【Ingredients】

8 mushrooms, a banch of golden mushroom, a small cube of vegetarian ham, a small cube of carrot and bamboo shoot, 1 small bowl of cornstarch, basil

【Seasoning】

(A)1 tbsp. of low sodium salt, 1 tbsp. of vegetarian oyster sauce, 1 tbsp. of soy sauce, 1 tbsp. of sugar.

(B)1 tbsp. of white sesame oil, 1 tbsp. of cornstarch.

【Methods】

❶ Blanch the golden mushroom, shred carrot and bamboo shoot.

❷ Keep the mushroom soft and cut the stem off, Strip and put cornstarch on and fry.

❸ Heat oil, fry vegetarian ham, vegetarian eel,bamboo shoot, carrot, golden mushroom, add (A) in then thicken.

翡翠鲍鱼

【材料】
素鸡···250 克
酸菜心·· 1 个
胡萝卜·· 1 根
平 菇 ·· 5 朵
草菇···200 克
油菜···250 克

【调味料】
(A)料：低钠盐 2 小匙、米酒 1 大匙、素高汤 1 碗、胡
　　椒少许。
(B)料：香油 2 大匙、淀粉 1 大匙。

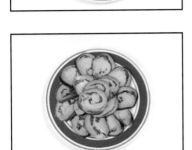

【作法】
❶ 素鸡炸至金黄色后切片。
❷ 香菇泡软。酸菜心、胡萝卜、平菇均切长片状，
　 与草菇一起入沸水煮 2 分钟后捞出放凉备用。
❸ 油菜氽烫后放入冰水中 30 秒，捞出备用。
❹ 备一圆盘依序排入胡萝卜、酸菜、平菇、素鸡，
　 加(A)料放入蒸笼中以大火蒸 10 分钟后取出，多
　 余汤汁加少许盐、酱油勾薄芡，再淋上香油即
　 可。

Abalone Mushroom with Vegetables

【Ingredients】
250g. vegetarian chicken, 1 black Mushroom, 1 pickled sour kale, 1 carrot, 5 abalone mushroom, 200g.
mushroom, 250g. rape

【Seasoning】
(A)2 tbsp. of low sodium salt, 1 tbsp. of rice wine, 1
　　bowl of vegetable broth, pepper.
(B)2 tbsp. of white sesame oil, 1 tbsp. cornstarch.

【Methods】
❶Fry the vegetarian chicken till golden, then slice.
❷Keep the black mushroom soft. Slice pickled sour
　rape, carrot, abalone mushroom, and cook with
　mushroom in boiling water for 2 minutes, cool them
　down.
❸Blanch the rape, cool down for 30 seconds, drain
　and garnish on th edge of the dish.
❹Put the carrot, pickled sour rape, abalone mushroom,
　vegetarian chicken orderly on a round dish. Add (A)
　in and steam for 10 minutes, pour out the soup, add
　salt, soy sauce, thicken, then spread white sesame
　oil.

鱼香茄子

【材料】

茄子……………………2 条
香菇……………………4 朵
素火腿…………………1 小块
红辣椒…………………1 根
香菜…………………… 少许

【调味料】

(A)料：低钠盐、糖、辣椒酱
　各 1 小匙、酱油 1 大匙。
(B)料：淀粉 1 大匙。

【作法】

❶ 茄子去蒂洗净切块，香菇
　泡软去蒂切丁，素火腿切
　丁，红辣椒切末。
❷ 热油炸茄子，待茄子变软
　即可捞出沥油备用。
❸ 另起油锅，爆香香菇后倒
　入辣椒丝、素火腿拌炒，
　加入茄子、(A)料后勾芡，
　起锅前淋上香油，撒些香
　菜即可。

Fry Eggplant

【Ingredients】

2 eggplants, 4 black mushrooms,
1cube of vegetarian ham, 1
chilli, parsley

【Seasoning】

(A)1 tbsp. of low sodium salt,
　sugar, sweet-spicy sauce.
(B)1 tbsp. of cornstarch.

【Methods】

❶Cut the stems of eggplants
　off and cube and soften
　black mushroom. Cut the
　stems off and dice, dice the
　vegetarian ham, chop chilli.
❷Heat oil, fry eggplants till
　soft, drain.
❸ Heat anotherr oil, sante
　black mushroom, add chilli,
　chopped vegetarian ham to
　fry, put eggplants and (A)
　spicies on, thicken, spread
　white sesame oil, parsley
　before turn off.

蚂蚁上树

【材料】

粉丝 1 把、香菇 4 朵、胡萝
卜 1/4 根、玉米笋 2 根、荸荠
4 个、红辣椒、芹菜、香菜各
少许。

【调味料】

低钠盐 1 小匙、酱油 1 大匙、
糖 1 小匙、胡椒粉、淀粉、香
油各少许。

【作法】

❶ 粉丝入水泡软切成 4 段。
❷ 香菇、胡萝卜、玉米笋、
　荸荠、芹菜均切碎丁，红
　辣椒斜切。
❸ 起油锅，爆香香菇、红辣
　椒，再放入胡萝卜、玉米
　笋、荸荠及盐、酱油、糖、
　胡椒粉加适量水拌炒至熟
　后，将粉丝入锅焖熟。
❹ 起锅前倒入水淀粉勾芡，
　淋少许香油，撒上芹菜末
　盛后以香菜点缀。

Bean Threads with Vegetables

【Ingredients】

1 banch of bean threads, 4
black mushrooms, 1/4 carrot, 2
corncobs, 4 water chestnuts,
1 chilli, 1 celery, parsley

【Seasoning】

1 tbsp. of low sodium salt, 1
tbsp. of soy sauce, 1 tbsp. of
sugar. pepper, cornstarch,
white sesame oil.

【Methods】

❶Soften the bean threads, and
　quarter it.
❷Dice the black mushrooms,
　carrot, corncobs, water
　chestnuts, celery, slice
　chilli.
❸ Heat oil, sante black
　mushrooms, chilli, add
　carrot, corncobs, water
　chestnuts to fry, and put

salt, soy sauce, sugar, pepper, water on, stew with bean threads.
❹ Thicken by cornstarch, spread
white sesame oil, diced celery before truning off. Garnish by
parsley.

炸蔬菜

【材料】

胡萝卜	……………………………………	1 根
莲藕	……………………………………	1 节
青椒	……………………………………	1 个
四季豆	……………………………………	1 小把
茄子	……………………………………	1 个
蛋	……………………………………	1 个
煎炸粉	……………………………………	1 碗
水	……………………………………	1 碗

【调味料】

(A)料：酱油2小匙、姜泥一小撮。
(B)料：番茄酱适量。

【作法】

❶ 胡萝卜去皮切丝，莲藕去厚皮切薄片浸醋15分钟，茄子切片，青椒去籽切片，四季豆去头尾及侧筋洗净备用。

❷ 在大碗中打蛋，加水及煎炸粉搅匀，将所有材料一一裹面衣。

❸ 热油，小心放入 ❷ 的蔬菜油炸，待呈金黄色即可捞出沥油。可沾酱油加姜泥或番茄酱食用。

Fry Vegetables

【Ingredients】

1 carrot, 1 piece of lotus root, 1 green bell pepper, 1 banch of season bean, 1 eggplant, 1 egg, 1 bowl of fry flour, 1 bowl of water

【Seasoning】

(A)2 tbsp. of soy sauce, chopped ginger a little bit.
(B)Ketchup.

【Methods】

❶Strip and shred carrot, strip and slice thinly the lotus root and keep in vinegar water for 15 minutes. Slice eggplant, keep the seeds of green bell pepper away and slice, cut the top and bottom of season beans, strip the sides and clean.

❷Stir the egg in a big bowl, add water and fry flour, and put all ingredients in.

❸Heat oil, fry the ❷ vegetables carefully till golden, drain. Serve with ketchup or soy sauce and ginger chopped.

图书在版编目(CIP)数据

简易家常菜 / 林淑莲著.

北京：外文出版社，2002.6

(中华美食系列)

ISBN 7-119-03081-7

Ⅰ.简… Ⅱ.①林… Ⅲ.菜谱 - 中国 Ⅳ.TS972.182

中国版本图书馆 CIP 数据核字 (2002) 第 036782 号

外文出版社网址：
　http://www.flp.com.cn
外文出版社电子信箱：
　info@flp.com.cn
　sales@flp.com.cn

著作权合同登记图字：01-2002-1352
中文简体字版权由台湾华文网股份有限公司授权

中华美食系列(1)
简易家常菜

著　　者	林淑莲
责任编辑	刘　慧　刘承忠
印刷监制	韩少乙
出版发行	外文出版社
社　　址	北京市百万庄大街 24 号　　邮政编码　100037
电　　话	(010)68320579(总编室)
	(010)68329514 / 68327211(推广发行部)
制　　作	外文出版社照排中心
印　　刷	北京外文印刷厂
经　　销	新华书店 / 外文书店
开　　本	16 开(787 × 1092 毫米)　　字　数　30 千字
印　　数	3001-6000 册　　印　张　11.50
版　　次	2004 年第 1 版第 2 次印刷
装　　别	平
书　　号	ISBN 7-119-03081-7/J · 1602(外)
定　　价	80.00 元